48 DUCK SHOOTING - The Corcoran Gallery of Art.

William Ranney

Painter of the Early West

by

Francis S. Grubar
Assistant Professor, Department of Art
University of Maryland

FOREWORD

BY

Hermann Warner Williams, Jr.
Director, The Corcoran Gallery of Art

Clarkson N. Potter, Inc./Publisher
NEW YORK

FOREWORD

This definitive catalogue of the paintings and drawings of William Ranney accompanies the first retrospective exhibition of his works. It has long been the policy of the Corcoran Gallery to organize each year at least one major exhibition of the work of an outstanding American artist or group of artists. Because of the renewed and widespread interest in many of the neglected artists of the mid-nineteenth century, it is appropriate that we look again at this typically American painter known especially for his sporting, genre and Western scenes. Ranney's popularity during his lifetime is well attested by the flood of engravings and lithographs of his paintings that spread over the country as well as by his many imitators and copyists.

In organizing the exhibition we are particularly indebted to the grandson of the artist, Claude J. Ranney, who has for many years collected material on his grandfather's biography and his work. He has not only made his records and personal collection of Ranney's paintings and drawings available to us but has, with his daughter, Mrs. J. Maxwell Moran, contributed substantially to defraying the expense of this book. Assistant Professor Francis S. Grubar of the University of Maryland, after months of painstaking research, has written the biography and prepared the catalogue of all the known works of the painter.

Among the members of the staff who have contributed to the realization of this endeavor are Mrs. Ralph E. Phillips, Curator, who has assumed responsibility for the exhibition, Mrs. A. Robert Forbes, Registrar, who has taken care of administrative details, and Mr. Gudmund Vigtel, Assistant Director, who planned the installation.

We feel that the works which have been assembled to form this retrospective study of Ranney's work represent him at his best, and it is with the sincerest appreciation that we thank the museums and the individual owners for their kindness in allowing these key examples of the artist's work to be more widely known not only to the visitors to the exhibition but to the even wider audience who will refer to the book in the years ahead.

HERMANN WARNER WILLIAMS, JR.
DIRECTOR
THE CORCORAN GALLERY OF ART

ACKNOWLEDGMENTS

A work of this type would hardly be possible without the generous assistance of many individuals in various fields. A special debt of gratitude is due Mr. Claude J. Ranney for his untiring energy and interest in collecting works by his grandfather and assembling data which have proved invaluable. In the absence of correspondence or other records of the artist, his personal recollections aided in gaining a further insight into William Ranney's environment.

Several institutions have been of great help; in particular, the staff of the Corcoran Gallery of Art, especially Mr. Henri Dorra, Mrs. A. Robert Forbes, Mrs. Ralph E. Phillips, Miss Carolyn Smith, and Mr. Hermann Warner Williams, Jr.; the staffs of the Cincinnati Public Library, the Frick Art Reference Library, the Library of Congress, the Maryland Historical Society, the Mystic Maritime Museum, the National Academy of Design, the New York Historical Society, the New York Public Library, the Texas State Library and Historical Commission, and my colleagues at the University of Maryland.

In addition to the cooperation received from the owners of works by Ranney, whose names are cited in this catalogue, I wish to express my gratitude to the following individuals: Dr. E. Maurice Bloch, Mr. T. Gilbert Brouillette, Mr. James B. Byrnes, Mr. Kenneth R. Erfft, Mr. Ralph Fanning, Mrs. Anne Blake Freedberg, Miss Mildred Goosman, Mr. W. E. Groves, Mr. John J. Grubar, Mr. P. S. Harris, Mr. Edward S. Harrison, Jr., Mr. R. B. Honeyman, Jr., Professor Laurence A. Leite, Mr. C. Burr McCaughen, Mr. George F. McMurray, Mr. Clyde Newhouse, Mr. Harry Shaw Newman, Mr. Vernon C. Porter, Miss Ruth Shevin, Miss Dorothy L. Smith, Mr. Victor D. Spark, Miss Anne K. Stolzenbach, Mrs. Marian T. Terry, Mr. Robert C. Vose, Mr. Rudolf Wunderlich, and Mr. Philip Zorn.

F. S. G.

WILLIAM RANNEY

PAINTER OF THE EARLY WEST

The inception and development of an important school of American genre painting during the first three quarters of the nineteenth century coincided almost exactly in terms of time with the rise of its more famous counterpart, the American landscape school. For the most part, both schools were a rather casual grouping of artists who specialized in certain situations or locales, their common bond being one of subject matter and, to a lesser degree, technique and style. Both were products of the emergence of the young Republic, with its intense, understandable pride in nationalism, and its awareness and recognition of the common man. The tremendous Western land expansion, renewing the earlier impetus for exploration, adventure and settlement, the growth of our cities through the continuing influx of immigrants from Europe, and the development of industry and commerce, created an impact on American life which formed the groundwork for new outlooks, tastes and modes of expression. Colonial and Old World aristocratic traditions and customs gradually gave way to democratic ideals and standards.

By mid-nineteenth century a rising class of potential art patrons had emerged to take their places in the hallowed circle already established by their more informed and wealthier brethren. This new art consciousness, often naïve in taste but usually not lacking in enthusiasm, was nurtured in part by the increase in the number and quality of newspapers and literary magazines, which offered frequent columns on art activities, and the appearance of an early school of American art criticism and history, led by Henry T. Tuckerman, William Dunlap, C. Edwards Lester, John Durand, E. Anna Lewis, Margaret Fuller Ossoli, and James Jackson Jarvis. America's first art magazines materialized at this time in the form of the American Art-Union's *Transactions* and *Bulletins*, *The International Art-Union Journal*, *The Crayon*, and *The Cosmopolitan Art Journal*.

The establishment and development of institutions such as the American Academy, the Boston Athenaeum, the Pennsylvania Academy of Fine Arts, the National Academy of Design, and various art unions and numerous local groups, sponsoring exhibitions and providing instructional facilities, stimulated a growing awareness and interest in art. Galleries conducted by these and an increasing number of art dealers offered a variety of visual experiences to an interested public. Proprietors of the panoramas, dioramas, and cosmoramas conducted a brisk trade, judging from the advertisements and commentaries in the publications of the day. Art auctions were numerous, as well as fairs and exhibitions of all types, few of which were without some form of artistic representation. Prints supplied by Currier and Ives, and others, permeated the social and economic fabric of our society by making a type of art available to all, and photography as a new art form was first being realized. The visual hunger of our populace sought and found many outlets of expression.

Within this framework developed an interesting if not impressive school of American genre painting. A hard and fast line of demarcation between the artists who would be called members of the school and those who would not, might be difficult to assess firmly in many individual cases, for most artists painted an occasional anecdotal scene at this time. On the other hand, many genre artists painted portraits, landscapes, and historical works. In general, however, the genre school would be composed of those artists who emphasized painting of everyday life as their major *forte*, with the stress centering on an incidental aspect of it. Stylistically, because of the nature of their emphasis, most members of this school would be inclined to embrace some form of realism as a means of attaining their desired results.

Among the many artists who may be assigned to the American genre school, the earliest to appear in the first quarter of the nineteenth century were John Lewis Krimmel (1789-1821), Henry Sargent (1770-1845), Alvan Fisher (1792-1863), William Chappel (active during 1806-1813), Henry Inman (1801-1846), and, the real leader of the movement, William Sidney Mount (1807-1868). The rapid growth of popularity and interest in genre painting is marked by the increased number of practitioners working in the second and third quarters of the century, the heyday of the school's development. A list of some of the more significant genre artists during this period would include: Eastman Johnson (1824-1906), George Caleb Bingham (1811-1879), David Gilmour Blythe (1815-1865), Richard Caton Woodville (1825-1855), John George Brown (1831-1913), Edward Lamson Henry (1841-1919), George Catlin (1796-1872), Charles Deas (1818-1867), George Henry Durrie (1820-1863), Seth Eastman (1808-1875), Karl Bodmer (1809-1893), Arthur Fitzwilliam Tait (1819-1905), Karl Ferdinand Wimar (1828-1862), John Mix Stanley (1814-1872), Alfred Jacob Miller (1810-1874), John Quidor (1801-1881), Charles Christian Nahl (1818-1878), Frank or Francis Blackwell Mayer (1827-1899), Thomas LeClear (1818-1882), John Whetten Ehninger (1827-1889), Albertis D. O. Browere (1814-1887), Robert Walter Weir (1803-1889), Thomas Waterman Wood (1823-1903), Francis William Edmonds (1806-1863), Lily Martin Spencer (1822-1902), George Cochran Lambdin (1830-1896), Charles F. Blauvelt (1824-1900), John Thomas Peele (1822-1897), George Whiting Flagg (1816-1897), Tompkins Harrison Matteson (1813-1884), Enoch Wood Perry, Jr. (1831-1915), Horace Bonham (1835-1892), and James Goodwyn Clonney (1812-1867), all contemporaries of William Ranney.

Thomas Eakins (1844-1916) and Winslow Homer (1836-1910) exhibited strong enough tendencies in their earlier efforts to warrant inclusion within this group. In fact, as Lloyd Goodrich has pointed out, a climax in the development of American genre painting of the nineteenth century was reached in the work of these two notable artists.[1] However, if their earlier paintings can be said to have demonstrated a triumph of genre painting, their later directions, conversely, reflected its decline as well. Post-Civil War American taste may still have retained a lingering attachment for indigenous themes, but this was gradually displaced and superseded by a new wave of influences emanating from Europe. The simple, homely themes paled before the art for art's sake credo. Not until the advent of "The Eight" in the first decade of the twentieth century would genre again be given a significant role in American painting.

William Ranney appeared on the scene as a professional artist shortly before 1840, at a time when the American genre school was on the verge of entering its most flourishing and prolific period. Although he tried his hand at other branches of painting – portrait, historical, and landscape – usually with creditable results, it was essentially in the field of genre, and more specifically, his interpretation and rendition of Western and sporting scenes, that he made his most significant contributions.

He was born in Middletown, Connecticut, on May 9, 1813, of parents who were descendants of early Scotch-English settlers.[2] Clarissa Gaylord Ranney, his mother, was born on January 22, 1789, and died on December 16, 1863. She was the daughter of Samuel Gaylord, a Revolutionary patriot, and Azubah Atkins. Captain Samuel Gaylord, Clarissa's grandfather, had served in the French and Indian Wars. The Gaylord forebears were said to have arrived at Dorchester, Massachusetts, from Plymouth, England, in 1630.

The artist's father, Captain William Ranney, was born in Middletown, November 30, 1783. One of Captain Ranney's ancestors was Thomas Ranney (c. 1616-June 21, 1713) of Scotland, who arrived in Middletown in 1658, and was credited with being the last survivor of the settlers of Middletown when he died there at the age of ninety-seven.[3] Captain Ranney married Clarissa Gaylord on November 16, 1808. Records of the Mystic Maritime Museum in Mystic, Connecticut, list fifteen commands under Captain Ranney in the West Indian and other trades, among them the sloop *Grey Hound*, which was captured while attempting to run the British blockade in 1814. He was lost at sea with his last command, the brig *Union*, on a passage from St. Croix to Middletown, probably in February, 1829.[4]

Little is known of William Ranney's early youth. One might have expected that his father's occupation would have offered some attraction to young Ranney. However, so far as is known, he expressed no desire to follow a maritime career. The luster of Middletown's earlier successes in shipping was no longer as bright as it had been three-quarters of a century before and probably offered little attraction at this time to an ambitious youth. While there are a few sketches and a marine painting here and there among his *oeuvre*, this theme was only an incidental aspect of his later effort. His quest for adventure would lead him into a far different clime.

William Ranney's middle name is often included in later accounts of his life or work. The usual spelling is "Tylee"; however, "Tiley" and "Tilley" appear also in the genealogy of the Ranney family. Tuckerman and others recorded his middle initial incorrectly as "S". In any case, the artist discarded his middle name early in his career. It did not appear in the pay vouchers issued from the Texan Army in 1836,[8] the diploma awarded for a painting exhibited with the Mechanics' Institute in New York in 1838,[9] or on his business card (p. 8), or on the scrap of paper containing his signature in 1854 (No. 209), and in the city directories for the 1840's.[11, 12] Nor is any painting or drawing known to have been signed by him using the middle initial.

In 1826, at the age of thirteen, William Ranney went to Fayetteville, North Carolina, where his uncle, William Nott, was established as a merchant.[5] Presumably the family intended that the youth should make a career in business. This was not destined to be the case, however, for after a short term with his uncle, he was said to have wearied of the countinghouse and next was apprenticed to a tinsmith, also in Fayetteville, with whom he worked for some six years. There is no evidence in his life up to this point to indicate any artistic inclination, though it has been suggested that he may have begun to sketch while in North Carolina.[6]

These must have been impressionable years for the young artist-to-be. Undoubtedly it was during this period that he was first exposed to the stories of Daniel Morgan, Francis Marion, Daniel Boone, and the life and customs of the ante-bellum South in general. Later, these impressions would crystallize in such paintings as THE BATTLE OF COWPENS (No. 6), MARION CROSSING THE PEDEE (No. 56), DANIEL BOONE AND HIS COMPANIONS DISCOVERING KENTUCKY (Nos. 38, 39), THE VIRGINIA WEDDING (No. 80), and others.

After completing his apprenticeship sometime in 1833 or 1834, Ranney returned to the North where he apparently began to study drawing and painting in Brooklyn. Most sources agree on this point, but none elaborate further with regard to where he studied or under whom. Little additional information has been discovered in the course of this study which might further clarify the problem.[7] It is certain, however, that whatever interest Ranney had in acquiring formal artistic instruction at this time, it was shelved temporarily in favor of an irresistible lure from the Southwest — the Texan struggle for independence from Mexico.

A decade and a half earlier, in 1819, another Connecticut Yankee, Moses Austin, had been responsible for initiating the plan which first brought the Americans to Texas, when he obtained permission from Spain to establish an American colony there. Spain agreed to give land and grant tax and customs exemptions in exchange for the political and religious affiliation of the settlers. Shortly after, Mexico succeeded in gaining her independence from Spain, and Texas became a part of Mexico.

After the death of Moses Austin in 1821, his son, Stephen F. Austin, succeeded in putting the original plan into effect, and some twenty thousand American frontiersmen and pioneers flocked into Texas during the 1820's and early thirties. Increasing friction over matters of taxation, religion, political representation, customs duties, local rule and slavery, developed with the Mexican government. When, in 1836, President Santa Ana proclaimed a unified constitution, ended states' rights, and attempted to prevent further immigration from America, the American settlers' anger flared into open revolt. Their heroic and tragic stand at the Alamo (February 23 to March 6, 1836), where some two hundred Texans withstood the attacks of three thousand Mexican troops for twelve days before they were defeated and annihilated, created a rallying symbol. The battle cry "Remember the Alamo" fired the blood of many a young American intent on adventure or imbued with patriotic or idealistic zeal to aid his countrymen. Europe had her Napoleonic campaigns and Greek and Italian wars for independence which provided some motivation for fostering the romantic impulse. For the American in the Eastern cosmopolitan centers, already stamped with the signs of an emerging industrial culture, the natural and human challenges of the frontier probably held a similar appeal.

After a visit with his relatives in North Carolina, William Ranney departed for New Orleans and enlistment in the Texan cause. Pay records in the

Texas State Archives indicate that he was in the Texan Army from March 12 to November 23, 1836.[8] He enlisted in the company of one Captain Hubbel and later served under Captain Fowler. Family tradition claims that he was on the guard detail placed over Santa Ana, who had been captured after the battle of San Jacinto, April 21, 1836. According to notes in the possession of the artist's grandson, Claude J. Ranney, William Ranney was subsequently appointed regimental paymaster through the influence of Major Wells, a fellow townsman, and remained in that capacity until his tour of duty was completed. It is believed that in addition to being paid in money, he was also given land grants, his deed calling for what is now a portion of Austin, Texas.

With reference to thematic material, the Texan experience emerges as one of the most important and vivid influences on Ranney's career. While no sketchbook or other specific works from this period are known for certain, some of the drawings and perhaps several of the preparatory paintings which have survived suggest on-the-spot recordings in their simple and direct interpretations of prairie life. Unlike Winslow Homer, Edwin Forbes or the Wauds, in the Civil War period, the professional and transitory aspects of army life did not seem to offer much attraction for Ranney. Unfortunately, perhaps, no battle of San Jacinto, the Alamo, or meeting of Santa Ana and Houston appear among his paintings. Instead, it was his contact with the adventurous life of the hardy prairie and mountain men — the trappers, guides, traders, hunters, in their characteristic terrain — which intrigued him. Many of these had responded to the Texan predicament and served in that cause. Their picturesque dress, habits and manners, techniques, stories and horses had a lasting effect on the young artist. HUNTING WILD HORSES (No. 21), THE LASSO (No. 20), THE PRAIRIE FIRE (No. 32), THE TRAPPER'S LAST SHOT (No. 42), THE RETREAT (No. 51), and others, remain as tangible evidence of the acuteness and sureness of his vision. Strangely enough, however, almost a decade passed before he would undertake these subjects in earnest.

After his war experience, the young artist returned to Brooklyn in 1837 and resumed his art studies. He received his first commission and public notice the following year when his PORTRAIT OF MR. THOMPSON, 35 YEARS' PORTER OF MERCHANTS' BANK (No. 5) was exhibited at the National Academy of Design. Later that same year he was awarded a diploma for his painting, A COURTING SCENE (No. 4), which was exhibited at the Mechanics' Institute Fair of 1838. The Institute, as its name implied, placed its emphasis on the mechanical arts.[9] However, there were paintings other than by Ranney on exhibition at their Fair that year. The *New York Evening Post for the Country*, September 12, 1838, offered no comment on Ranney's work but mentioned the miniature paintings of William H. Miller (c. 1820-after 1860) ". . . who appears to be an artist of merit." Apparently the critic's major criterion was based on the fact that ". . . we recognized the faces of some among the collection."

Almost nothing is known of Ranney's activities between 1839 and 1842. One contemporary source suggested that he returned to Fayetteville, where he remained with his uncle, William Nott, until the latter's death in 1840.[10] Claude J. Ranney thought he might have made another trip to Texas in connection with his land claims. Whatever the case, Ranney was back in New York City by 1843, where he was recorded in the City's directories for 1843-1845 as a portrait painter, 20 Chambers Street.[11] In 1846-1847 his address was listed as New York University.[12] A rather ornate business card, which he probably designed, was printed at this time with the following information: "William Ranney, / Portrait Painter / No. 30 University / New York" (No. 208). His name did not appear in subsequent New York City directories. The American Art-Union *Transactions* for 1847 and 1848 recorded a change of residence to Weehawken, New Jersey.

In 1848, in New York, Ranney married Margaret Agnes O'Sullivan. She was born in Cork, Ireland, on January 7, 1819, and had survived her husband by almost half a century when she died in West Hoboken, New Jersey, on August 19, 1903. The fine portrait of his wife (No. 52), perhaps painted about 1850, must rank among his better efforts in that category. Claude J. Ranney fondly recalls that she was a sensitive person, well-educated (she could quote from the Bible and Shakespeare), and unquestionably was an important and constructive influence upon the life of his grandfather. She became acquainted with and was accepted into the circle of such influential personages of the day as the members of the Stevens family of Hoboken, among others.[13]

After several years in Weehawken, the Ranneys probably moved back to New York for a short while, where their first son, William, was born on March 27, 1850. The same year, Ranney was elected an Associate Member of the National Academy of Design.[14] James Joseph, the younger son, was born three years later, on November 1, 1853, after the family had settled permanently in West Hoboken, New Jersey. There Ranney built a rather quaint homestead which stood for three-quarters of a century (No. 210). It was among the first homes erected in the vicinity, located on the southwest corner of Thirteenth Street and Palisades Avenue (now Union City, New Jersey). The house was demolished in 1927 to make room for an apartment building. Ranney owned almost the entire block from Twelfth to Thirteenth streets and New York to Palisades avenues, on which he paid about two dollars per year in taxes!

Hoboken had first been settled by the Dutch as early as 1640. Its growth was slow until the financier, Colonel John Stevens, developed the area as a suburban resort for New Yorkers during the second quarter of the nineteenth century. On August 31, 1850, *The Home Journal* recorded the census of Hoboken as 2,750, estimating an increase of 1,000. About one hundred new homes had been erected ". . .many first class." Particularly during the hot summer months, the New York newspapers and magazines made frequent references to the pleasant aspects of Hoboken. A sampling of a few of these would give reasons why this was true, and why, perhaps, the Hoboken area would have appealed to a man with a love for the out-of-doors, yet whose work would have profited by being near the New York exhibition center.

New-York Enquirer, March 29, 1828: Hoboken. This delightful place is again becoming the resort of fashion. By a new arrangement in Mr. Stevens' line of steamboats, four will run hourly from the foot of Barclay-street, so that the means of conveyance will be accessible to everyone. Hoboken is the most salubrious of our suburban villages, commanding a prospect exceeded by none in our country; possessing a variety of beautiful scenery. It is about twenty minutes walk from Weehawken Bluff, which is so immortalized by the pen of Halleck, and is the commencement of the stupendous range of palisades, which are the admiration of all strangers for their picturesque wildness. In no place can a retreat be found from the heat of summer more delightfully refreshing – the cool breeze from the water is wafted into the beautiful promenade in front of Van Boskerk's Hotel, and hundreds are seen reposing under the spacious shade of the magnificent trees which adorn the walks. No resident of our city can be ignorant of its beauties, and few strangers pass through without becoming acquainted with them.

The Knickerbocker, November, 1848, p. 467: When there comes a warm autumnal rainy day, it gives us great enjoyment to go over (*omnes solus*) to Hoboken, and repair to a gable-angle of the Swiss châlet, built by the tasteful Stevens, and there, under an open "weather-board" canopy, gaze for hours upon the distant city, spreading before us like a map, and our noble harbor and bay, covered with tall ships, their tapering masts and cordage pencilled against the sky, or the lighter craft, with their white sails glinting for an instant in the fitful sunlight that steals through a broken cloud. There we watch . . . .

New-York Herald, July 15, 1850: Fashionable Promenades . . . Elysian Fields, Hoboken. Mr. J. C. Stevens to put in a gravel drive through the Fields and around the shore . . . Hoboken is a beautiful spot for retirement, and is much enjoyed, particularly by foreigners, whose quiet, respectable behavior contrasts favorably with that of some who think an hour's liberty should be turned into licentiousness and depraved lawlessness. More than fifteen thousand persons visit Hoboken every fine Sunday . . .

Ibid., July 13, 1857: The Elysian Fields On A Sunday . . . And of the many delightful resorts with which the vicinity of New York abounds, probably none is a greater favorite than the far famed Elysian Fields at Hoboken . . .

Even Mrs. Trollope responded favorably to these pleasant surroundings. Her *Domestic Manners of the Americans* contains an account of a visit to Hoboken in which she commented on the beautiful walks, shrubs, and picturesque view. However, she probably could not resist ending her description by stating that of the many thousands of persons scattered about, nineteen out of twenty were men. "The ladies," she wrote, "were at church."

In addition to William Ranney, a number of artists found the area in and around Hoboken attractive. William Mason Brown, Charles Loring Elliott, Paul La Croix, Robert W. Weir, and Thomas W. Whitley resided and worked in Hoboken, and Andrew Melrose and James E. Butterworth in West Hoboken. The famous landscape painter, Asher B. Durand, although living in New York, often took the Stevens ferry to the Elysian Fields to paint directly from nature. In an article about Durand in *The Art Quarterly*, Spring, 1945, Frederick A. Sweet stated ". . . there he did careful oil studies direct from nature, having prepared his palette at home, and brought along a portable easel and camp stool. Durand was undoubtedly the first to inaugurate this practice of painting out-of-doors and the character of his work was very much determined by it."

Some of Ranney's smaller oil studies and pencil or pen-and-ink sketches have the vigor, spontaneity and simplified but bold modeling usually identified with this practice (Nos. 110-113). However, his large, finished

1*

paintings were undoubtedly painted in the studio, which was the usual procedure followed by most of the artists of the first half of the nineteenth century.

Ranney's studio, which occupied the entire north side, was the unique feature of his home. Probably Henry T. Tuckerman, the poet, art critic and historian, visited the artist in the 1850's and was startled to find a studio which contrasted so much with artists' studios in the city. He described it later in his *Book of the Artists*, 1867, as being

...so constructed as to receive animals; guns, pistols, and cutlasses hung on the walls; and these, with curious saddles and primitive riding gear, might lead a visitor to imagine he had entered a pioneer's cabin or border chieftain's hut; such an idea would, however, have been at once dispelled by a glance at the many sketches and studies which proclaimed that an artist, and not a bushranger, had here found a home.

Claude J. Ranney, the artist's grandson, remembers the Ranney homestead well.[15] He described it as a large, glassed-in studio, two stories high, on the north side; the family lived on the other side of the house, which had about fourteen rooms. The structure was probably built by the artist, incorporating some rather unusual ideas, such as peculiar roof lines. Spacious grounds surrounded the house, and a picket fence encircled the whole property. There were hawthorn, boxwood hedges and other decorative shrubs and trees. Nearby was a stable for the artist's horses – for he loved to ride as well as to use them for models. A cedar summerhouse for the children was located near the stable. All in all, it is a description of what must have been a very pleasant home.[16]

Contemporary accounts described Ranney as a well-liked person – kind, courteous and modest. He had many friends among the members of his profession. Indeed, the well-known genre painter William Sidney Mount was supposed to have called him "...a glorious fellow!"[17] As late as 1911, during the anniversary celebration of the incorporation of West Hoboken, it was stated that "his amiable and courteous greetings are remembered by many of the early residents here..."[18] Indicative, perhaps, of the warm feelings most people seemed to have for William Ranney, as well as giving some expression of his rising popularity, was the humorous anecdote about the artist which was printed in *The Knickerbocker*, for January, 1854, pages 546-47:

...'Tis not often that a joke is cracked on the head of an artist; but it so happened a few days since, that a distinguished literary gentleman and military officer on a visit to Mr. Ranney, the historical painter, had the temerity to indulge in one. On arriving at the lodge of Mr. Ranney, which is penned in by a neat fence, he found the artist lustily employed with his maul-stick in walloping some cows out of his enclosure. "So ho! Mr. Ranney," said one of the party, "I expected to have found you employed on the Siege of Yorktown; but I see you stick to the 'battle of the cow-pens'." Mr. Ranney has given the world some fine historical pictures on the Revolution.

It was not by mere chance that some of William Ranney's finest paintings are found in the sporting category, for he was an ardent sportsman. He was fond of outdoor sports of various kinds, hunting in particular.[19] DUCK SHOOTERS (No. 36), ON THE WING (Nos. 45, 46), DUCK SHOOTING (No. 48), and DUCK SHOOTER'S PONY (No. 70) are dramatic portrayals of action which exhibit the intensity, assuredness and knowledge of the direct participant, rather than the sometimes superficial response of the vicarious spectator.

Ranney was said to have been one of the founders of the New York Cricket Club, organized in 1843, which utilized the Elysian Fields in Hoboken as their home grounds. The New York newspapers followed the team's progress with great interest in its matches with Philadelphia, Paterson, Newark, Winterville (Connecticut), and other clubs. Ranney played with the first eleven until the end of the 1854 season.[20] Curiously, no painting or drawing devoted to this theme has been discovered in his work.

The fact that his name did not appear on the New York Club roster as a player during the following year or thereafter is significant. Doubtless the illness which was to prove fatal must have struck him at this time. During his last three years, there was a noticeable decline in the number of paintings submitted to the National Academy of Design exhibitions, or done for patrons elsewhere. He died of consumption at his home in West Hoboken on November 18, 1857, after being given the last rites of the Catholic Church. Although a Protestant by birth,[21] Ranney became a Catholic during his last days through the intercession of his wife, Margaret, and Bishop James Roosevelt Bayley, also a convert. The funeral service took place at St. Mary's Catholic Church, Hoboken, and the burial in Bergen Cemetery, overlooking the countryside he had painted with such understanding in so many of his works. Ironically, only one fellow artist, Charles Loring Elliott, the portrait painter, attended the funeral. Perhaps it was due, as the *New-York Times*, November 24, 1857, suggested ". . . to Mr. Ranney's comparative isolation for many years, and not to the studious neglect of his contemporaries." That these artists would vindicate themselves one year later by rallying under the cause of the Ranney Fund Sale, was amply proved by the success of that venture.

The Ranney Fund exhibition and sale was held at the National Academy of Design, New York, in December, 1858, over a year after the artist's untimely death.[22] Its major purpose was to provide financial security for his widow and children by disposing of the paintings and drawings which remained in his studio. Judging from an article which appeared in the New York *Evening Post*, December 11, 1858, Ranney himself, with understandable concern for the welfare of his family, expressed this idea just before he died.[23] The same article discussed in some detail the family's financial condition, which may have been somewhat overstated.

Mr. Ranney owned a small cottage [?] in Hoboken, on which there is a lien of about $800, and also about $200 of smaller debts. . . . On his sick-bed, a few days before he breathed his last breath, Mr. Ranney said to a friend: "If I only had two weeks' more strength, these sketches could be finished up and enough procured from their sale to effect this object."

Little was done for the next six months after his death, when *The Crayon*, May, 1858, reported on page 148 ". . . we are requested to mention that the widow of the late William Ranney has left for disposal, with Mr. S. N. Dodge, No. 189 Chatham Square [the artists' supply store where Ranney purchased some of his materials] for the benefit of herself and children, the whole of the remaining art effects of her late husband. They consist of finished pictures, studies for pictures, sketches from Nature, and unfinished works, besides many fine pen and ink drawings, sketches in pencil, etc. . . ." The situation seemed destined to languish again, when several interested persons stepped forward and succeeded in putting into motion the movement which led to the final sale. The artist, Thomas S. Cummings, a member of the National Academy and compiler of that Institution's *Historic Annals*, 1865, gave the major credit to Nason B. Collins and the painters Arthur F. Tait and William Hart.

Unquestionably, the organizational leader was Collins, a young New York merchant. On November 19, 1858, he sent printed invitations to collectors of Ranney's work, such as Joseph Moreau, asking if they would be willing to loan their paintings to the exhibition. (See Appendix.) No catalogue of Ranney paintings which may have been loaned is known; the newspapers and periodicals, which responded generously to this cause during the month of December of that year recorded nothing about loaned pictures, but concentrated their remarks entirely on the works which were to be sold. Some ninety-five fellow artists responded and donated paintings for the sale. The list is a veritable *Who's Who* in art for that period. Among the well-known artists were McEntee, Inness, Richards, Gifford, Cropsey, Hicks, Durand, the Harts, Casilear, Gray, Ehninger, Bierstadt, Gignoux, Church, Kensett, Elliott, Tait, and a host of others. The National Academy offered its rooms for the event.

On December 9, 1858, a public lecture on American art was given at Clinton Hall by the noted lawyer and friend of Ranney, James Topham Brady,[25] the proceeds of which defrayed the exhibition expenses. The auction sale itself, conducted without charge by H. H. Leeds and Company, took place on the nights of December 20 and 21, 1858, and netted over $7,000.[26] Three weeks later a meeting was held at which it was decided to appoint the executive officers of the National Academy, Asher B. Durand, Thomas S. Cummings, and Francis W. Edmonds, as Trustees to invest the money, paying the interest semi-annually to Mrs. Ranney.[27] In the event of her death, the payment would continue to the guardians of the children until they became of age, when the principal was to be turned over to them. In addition to the aid given the Ranney family, the success of the sale was instrumental in the formation of the important Artist's Fund Society.[28]

The *Fund Catalogue* of the Ranney sale recorded 212 works, of which 108 were by Ranney. These are included in a separate list in the Appendix. In most cases, only the title and artist's name were given for each entry, with little else to aid in their further identification. Undoubtedly the majority were small sketches and studies. Fortunately, a copy of the *Fund Catalogue* exists (in the New York Historical Society) which has inscribed on it the price paid and the buyer's name for each item. Possibly this was the copy used to keep a record at the sale, perhaps by Nason B. Collins.[24]

An interesting added note on the Ranney Fund sale appeared in *The Crayon*, December, 1860, page 353, in which the commentary was concerned with two line engravings which had just been published ". . .of a superior order . . . The next is an engraving by S. V. Hunt from Church's MORNING

IN THE TROPICS, a picture sold at the sale of the Ranney collection, and which is now engraved as a souvenir of that event."[29]

Ranney tried his hand at most types of subjects, portrait, historical, land-scape, genre, but it was primarily in one phase of art that he was best known during his period and in our own – his portrayal of the Western scene.

From the very beginnings of our country, Americans have been concerned with and deeply conscious of the implications of the West. Its magnetic force exerted a continuous stimulus to which generations of Americans responded, for a variety of reasons. However, the "West" was hardly a static concept, or even a place. That is, a man living seventy-five years ago would hardly be expected to have the same reaction to the term as one living two hundred years ago. In the Colonial period, the West was just over the Alleghenies in the Ohio Valley, Kentucky, western New England and New York. During the first half of the nineteenth century, in Ranney's generation, Texas and the areas following the great rivers, and California with its gold lure, constituted the West. The fluctuating, shifting position of the frontier marked the stages in our progress of securing final mastery over this vast territory. The story of America's development as a nation would not be complete until this had been achieved.

Frederick Jackson Turner's thesis concerning the significance of the frontier in American history, startling to those who heard him present it for the first time in 1893, and still controversial today, maintained:

Up to our own day American history has been in a large degree the history of the colonization of the Great West. The existence of an area of free land, its continuous recession, and the advance of American settlement Westward, explain American development.... Stand at Cumberland Gap and watch the procession of civilization, marching single file – the buffalo following the trail to the salt springs, the Indian, the fur trader and hunter, the cattle raiser, the pioneer farmer – and the frontier has passed by. Stand at South Pass in the Rockies a century later and see the same procession with wider intervals between....[30]

The key to the Turnerian thesis is not merely the recognition of the frontier as a physical factor. The real significance was its effect in motivating the mass migration of Americans.[31] This insatiable drive for mobility was expressed some fifty years before Turner by a contributor to the *New York Tribune*, April 1, 1843, who described the "true pioneer" as

Strange, restless beings.... Fearlessness, hospitality and independent frankness, united with restless enterprise and unquenchable thirst for novelty and change are the peculiar characteristics of the Western pioneer. With him there is always a land of promise farther West, where the climate is milder, the soil more fertile, better timber and finer prairie. And on – and on – on he goes, always seeking and never attaining the Pisgah of his hopes.

Ranney's attitude toward the West was essentially that of the genre artist, who approached his subject in a frank, faithful and realistic manner. He was not concerned with recording Western landscape for its own sake but, characteristic of his group, endeavored to weave a simple story within the fabric of the physical terrain. Contrary to the efforts of George Catlin, John Mix Stanley, Alfred Jacob Miller, Seth Eastman or Charles Wimar, Ranney's sympathies were directed more toward the white hunter, trapper, and pioneer rather than the Indian. His paintings convey little of the grandeur and magnificence of Nature in the sublime sense, as encountered in some of the landscapes of Thomas Cole, Frederick Church or Thomas Moran. Man is not the subordinate issue in his work, waiving rationality in favor of an ecstatic, emotional or pantheistic response to Nature. There is little of the majestic resonance or subjective implications which William Cullen Bryant extolled in his prophetic "The Prairie":

> ...the Gardens of the Desert, these
> For which the speech of England has no name –
> The boundless unshorn fields, where lingers yet
> The beauty of the earth ere man had sinned –
> The Prairies. I behold them for the first,
> And my heart swells, while the dilated sight
> Takes in the encircling vastness.

> *The Knickerbocker*, December, 1833

The immediate, transitory and momentary facets of the Western scene were the important facts for Ranney, and if these served to narrow the extent of his artistic range, they also acted equally as a check. The straining, tense figure in THE TRAPPER'S LAST SHOT (No. 42) and the protruding, rolling eyes of his mount describe a very real and imminent danger. His rendition of THE PRAIRIE BURIAL (No. 30), a scene which must have occurred frequently, effectively portrays the grief of the central group without resorting to the extreme histrionic devices employed by the stage of that day.

Even in what must be considered among his more successful historical paintings, such as DANIEL BOONE'S FIRST VIEW OF KENTUCKY (Nos. 38-39) or the FIRST NEWS OF THE BATTLE OF LEXINGTON (No. 26), he applied the genre formula of stressing the incidental. Boone is a youthful frontiersman, authentically garbed, and standing almost casually among his friends as he contemplates the view before him. In the Lexington painting, one minor incident, marked with the thoroughness of the genre artist in describing detail, is made to carry the weight of the full implications of the event. Ranney's MARION CROSSING THE PEDEE (No. 56) cannot be identified firmly as to the exact battle involved, but conveys the mood and atmosphere surrounding the partisan leader in a more convincing manner than the overly dramatic painting of the same period by Emanuel Leutze of WASHINGTON CROSSING THE DELAWARE. The effectiveness of these pictures, then, is brought out not only through Ranney's ability as a draughtsman, designer or colorist, but also because he understood the value of and utilized to full advantage the intrinsic qualities which made genre attractive to the artist and layman. That he did not overemphasize these elements in his better efforts by allowing them to become merely theatrical or melodramatic in an overbearing sense, or mawkishly sentimental, is an indication of his selectivity and taste as an artist.

The few family portraits by Ranney that survive give an incomplete picture of his efforts in this category. No commissioned portrait has been located, although a few are known from contemporary records. Critics rarely mentioned Ranney in this capacity. However, a good genre artist would obviously be expected to display some facility at interpreting the human figure.

In addition, the economic attraction of portraiture as a potentially surer means of livelihood would have to be considered. Although by Ranney's time the daguerreotypes and other photographic processes were beginning to make an inroad on what had once been considered the exclusive domain of the artist, and landscape, genre and historical painters were finding increasing vogue and support by the public, the services of the portrait painter were still in high demand. On several occasions Ranney was known to have included portraits of family members or friends as some of the figures in his genre compositions – a device commonly used by Mount, Woodville, Bingham, Stearns and others.

Ranney's bias in portraiture apparently leaned toward the European tradition, with emphasis on the English school. The most affected and mannered among the group of known portraits is that of the artist's mother, Clarissa Gaylord Ranney (No. 2). Eighteenth-century England is reflected in the smooth, slick technique and the pose with the sloping "Gainsborough-type" shoulders. The colors are harsher and less subtle than the more characteristic English artists, recalling perhaps the earlier work of Kneller or Lely.

The later portrait of his wife, Margaret (No. 52), is painted in a more straightforward, less affected manner. Reliance is still held on a darker palette, but the colors are fused more effectively and the work as a whole indicates a more proficient performance. A similar comparison may be made between the two self-portraits (Nos. 1, 87). An idealized, baroque-like gesture characterizes the early effort. In the later example, his brushwork is more expansive and the colors richly contrasted, forming a solidly modeled head of strong intensity and subjective appeal. An earlier effort, THE MATCH BOY (No. 11), perhaps more correctly classified as a genre portrait, demonstrates a warm sensitivity in the modeling of the head, and perhaps anticipates Duveneck's similar subject renditions of some thirty years later.

Contemporary critics usually compared Ranney's sporting paintings with those of Arthur Fitzwilliam Tait, whose work was popularized through the lithographs of Currier and Ives. Unquestionably the two have a great deal in common, both in spirit and content. However, Ranney's range seems to have been less limited and, in his best efforts in this category, DUCK SHOOTING (No. 48), ON THE WING (No. 45) and DUCK SHOOTERS (No. 36) probably surpassed Tait's similar renditions.

Independent of his treatment of content, an appraisal of Ranney's technical skill reveals a competence which validates placing him in a respectable position among our minor masters of the nineteenth century. Perhaps one would not consider him a colorist in the usual sense of the term, but his selection and use of color within his means compares very favorably with his contemporaries. More attractive than Seth Eastman or George Catlin – in some ways, a more pleasing colorist than Mount – several of his paintings which have been restored recently exhibit a surprising brightness and tonal treatment (HALT ON THE PRAIRIE, No. 44, and PRAIRIE BURIAL, No. 30). Perhaps one of his finest paintings in this regard is the large version of ADVICE ON THE PRAIRIE (No. 68), which contains some remarkably subtle and luminous passages. The atmospheric qualities and general treatment of Ranney's DUCK SHOOTERS (No. 36) would compare favorably with Bingham's THE TRAPPERS' RETURN in the Detroit Institute of Arts.

In his more effectively designed prairie pictures, Ranney emphasized the vastness of space and brilliant clarity of the sky by utilizing a relatively flat horizon line breaking across the painting just below the center, a device commonly found among marine painters, especially those of the Dutch school in the seventeenth century, or some of the nineteenth-century *plage* painters. This increased the sense of depth and space and afforded certain possibilities for achieving monumentality in his figures by allowing them to project against the prominent sky. THE TRAPPER'S LAST SHOT (No. 42), THE LASSO (No. 20), HUNTING WILD HORSES (No. 21), and HALT ON THE PRAIRIE (No. 44), contain the more obvious examples.

Paradoxically, the literal treatment of the major figures had a tendency to immobilize fluidity of movement through the compositions. Ranney painted in an age when most of the critics and public taste still clamored for the "high finish" and minute precision inspired by the Düsseldorf school. In a restrained subject, the effect was less noticeable; where action was implied, as for example in THE BATTLE OF COWPENS (No. 6) or THE RETREAT (No. 51), a kind of "frozen mobility" resulted – doubtless what Holger Cahill referred to when he characterized Ranney as a "static Remington." This stylistic petrification was certainly not unique with Ranney, but typified that age and, in fact, still persists among the magic realists of today. Ranney had artistic sense enough to temper the tautness of this manner with more open brushwork when he described the foliage and other subordinate accessories. In his oil sketches, such as the STUDY OF A LEDGE (No. 110) and STUDY OF A HORSE'S HOOF (No. 114) and in the many fine pen and ink, pencil, and crayon drawings (see especially the excellent STUDY FOR 'HUNTING WILD HORSES,' No. 130) he demonstrated the vigor and spontaneity he was capable of when not committed to a "finished" picture.

Ranney's contemporary reputation as an artist was, in part, aided by his association with several of the major artistic organizations of the country. The most important professional organization for artists of that day was the National Academy of Design. Ranney was elected an Associate of the Academy in 1850, and was included in that organization's annual exhibitions as early as 1838, and regularly from 1845 until his death.

He was a consistent and popular contributor to the American Art-Union from 1845 until its sudden and unexpected end some seven years later. The program initiated by the Art-Union caught the public fancy and during the height of its spectacular development from 1847 through 1851, enjoyed unprecedented national recognition and acclaim which must have exceeded the fondest aspirations of even its most enthusiastic supporters. The basic purpose of this remarkable nonprofit organization was to promote the work of American artists and, in spite of some antagonism – part of which was probably justified – it succeeded in bringing before the public the efforts of over two hundred and fifty artists. For a five-dollar fee, a member received one chance for an original painting or other art work raffled at the annual December meeting in New York, an engraving (increased later to as many as six), and the publications of the organization.[32]

In addition, a free exhibition gallery was maintained in New York City, open longer each day than most of our modern galleries. The American Art-Union was a manifestation of a democratic age, breathing new life into American art activity for, as James Thomas Flexner stated, "...it encouraged the people to regard paintings not as awesome objects of virtue, suitable only for the rich and for museums, but as pleasures that ordinary citizens could enjoy as they hung on the walls of simple living rooms.... The demise of the Art-Union under an irrelevant legal attack undoubtedly contributed to the subsequent swamping of the American market with a new wave of imported affectation...."[33]

Depictions stressing the activities of ordinary citizens, American scenery, literature, and history would obviously have found special favor among the Art-Union's committee of selection and with the general public. The flourishing state of our genre school at mid-nineteenth century owed no small debt to the policies and facilities provided by this organization. The names of Bingham, Mount, Edmonds, Ranney and Woodville were probably as familiar to Americans of the 1840's and fifties as Wood, Benton and Curry were to those of the 1930's.

Not as extensive in its number of subscribers, but perhaps second only to the American Art-Union (which it was modeled after and followed into oblivion) was the Western Art-Union, located in Cincinnati. Ranney was accorded a signal honor when his TRAPPER'S LAST SHOT was selected to be the source of the engraving awarded each member in 1850 (see No. 197). Ranney's painting was distributed in the raffle, along with the *pièce de résistance* – one of Hiram Powers' versions of his GREEK SLAVE.

NOTES

[1] Lloyd Goodrich, *American Genre, The Social Scene In Paintings And Prints (1800-1935)* (New York, 1935), pp. 7-9.
[2] The Department of Health, Bureau of Vital Statistics, Middletown, Connecticut, was unable to locate a birth record for William Ranney, the artist.
[3] The Ranney Memorial and Historical Association, Cromwell, Connecticut, *Founders, Fathers and Patriots of Middletown Upper Houses* (Middletown, 1903) [p. 1], "Thomas Ranney... married in 1659, at the age of 43, to Mary Hubbard, aged 17, daughter of George Hubbard of Middletown... left four sons and six daughters; presumably the first person buried in the 'North Society' burying ground [Old Cromwell Cemetery]...." The Ranney family hold a reunion at his grave each June.
[4] Captain Ranney's active career is graphically presented in the Mystic Maritime Museum files:

    1810-11: Master of the schooner *Harmony*, Middletown.
    1811: First Master of ship *Wanderer*, built in Middletown, 1811, 289 tons. Registered for foreign trade [probably kept in port by the embargo].
    1813: First Master of schooner *Bainbridge*, Middletown, built in 1813, 248 tons [probably in port during the war].
    December 16, 1813: First Master of newly built sloop *Grey Hound* of Middletown, 65 tons, which attempted to run the British blockades. Captured in 1814.
    January, 1814: Again Master of ship *Wanderer*, in port at Middletown.
    November 26, 1814-October 13, 1815: Master of sloop *Opposition*, built in Middletown, 1813, 56 tons.
    May 11, 1816: Master of brig *James* of Hartford, 178 tons, West Indian trade.
    October 1, 1816: Master of ship *Glenthorn*, Hartford, 319 tons.
    June 22, 1819-1822: Master of ship *Corso*, built in Middletown, 1819, 349 tons.

October, 1822: Sailed new ship *Othello*, 264 tons, to New York. Sold there in December, 1822.

December 4, 1822: Master of brig *Argo* of New York, 253 tons.

October 16, 1823: Master of sloop *Rising Sun* of Middletown, 66 tons, West Indian trade.

November 20, 1824: Master of brig *Nymph*, Middletown, 147 tons, newly built. Sold in New York.

May 13, 1825: Master of brig *Governor Griswald*, built in Middletown, 1811, 197 tons.

November 19, 1827: Master of brig *Union*, Middletown, 139 tons, built there in 1824. Length 78-5, B 23-6, D 8-9. Owners: Joseph W. Alsop, Jr., Joseph W. Alsop, Sr., and Henry Chauncey, all of Middletown. Lost at sea.

The inland port of Middletown, located on the west bank of the Connecticut River, reached its height of prosperity during the third quarter of the eighteenth century, concentrating on shipbuilding and the triangular trade of slaves, sugar and rum. It was Connecticut's largest city in 1756. British action against American shipping during the Revolutionary War and the War of 1812, plus increasing competition with more favorably situated ports, caused a gradual decline in this phase of Middletown's activity. The transition to early industrial development was already underway in the 1820's, when Captain Ranney and four or five other Middletown sea captains were still following the older tradition. However, now the usual passage had been shortened to St. Croix, St. Thomas or some other point in the West Indies – a trip which took about fifteen days each way.

Captain Ranney's destination during the trips made in his last ship, the brig *Union*, was generally the West Indian island of St. Croix, located approximately sixty-five miles southeast of Puerto Rico. At that time, the island was a Danish possession. It was purchased by the United States in 1917 and is now the largest of the Virgin Islands under United States control. The brig *Union* usually carried a cargo of sugar and rum on the return trip.

In an age when telegraphic or other rapid means of communication were unknown, information concerning the whereabouts of vessels once they had left port must have depended largely on chance encounters with other vessels, which would be dutifully logged and passed on for publication in the marine lists of newspapers after arrival in port. Fortunately, a standard procedure was followed. Each entry usually included the type of vessel, name, master's name, home port or destination, and other pertinent information. Because of the discrepancies and mystery in the information surrounding Captain Ranney's last voyage, an attempt was made to trace his activities with the brig *Union* from the time he assumed command. Although the efforts were only partially successful, the results give a clearer view of his movements during his last two years, and provide further corroboration for the date of the disaster, February, 1829, which was most generally cited in later nineteenth century sources. Of less importance to this study, perhaps, is the interesting account it provides of the movements of what must have been a typical trading vessel of that day.

Middlesex Gazette and General Advertiser [Middletown, Conn.] March 26, 1826: Port of Saybrook... Sailed... April 3. Brig *Union*, Ranney, St. Croix...; *New-York Enquirer*, November 27, 1827: Middletown, Nov. 27 – Cleared, ship *Osprey*, Gaylord, Martinico; brig *Union*, Rainey [sic], St. Croix; *Ibid.*, January 21, 1828: Norfolk, Jan. 17 – arr. brig *William Dimmock*, of Boston, 13 ds from St. Croix, (Bass End)... Left 3d inst. brigs *Union*, Rainey [*sic*], of Middletown, awaiting cargo. *Ibid.*, February 28, 1828: Arrived... Brig *Mentor*, Lindeer, of Blue Hill, 15 days from St. Croix... brigs... *Union*, Ranney, for Middletown, 4 days. *Ibid.*, March 4, 1828: Arrived, Ship *Superior*, Waire, 64 days from Liverpool, with dry goods, etc... Spoke 10th Feb. lat. 43 long. 30 50, Br Brig *Nora*, 70 ds from London for St. John – supplied them with provision – she expected to put into the Western Islands – they were in a state of starvation. 1st inst. lat. 43 long. 73, brig *Union*, Reynor [sic], of Middletown, fm St. Croix, for N. York, who kindly supplied us with provision. She [*sic*] S. has experienced very rough weather – lost sails and sprung a leak, and made 2½ feet water per hour... Arrived... Ship *Jupiter*... Left at S. Cr. 21st Feb... *Union*, Raney [sic] of do. [Middletown] for New York, sailed 5 ds before... Below, brig *Union*, of Middletown, Reynor [sic] 14 ds from St. Croix, with rum and sugar. *Ibid.*, March 6, 1828: Arrived... Brig *Union*, Bonney [*sic*], 15 days from St. Croix, with rum and sugar. *Ibid.*, Middletown, April 1 – Cleared, brig *Union*, Rainey [*sic*], St. Croix. *Connecticut Herald*, [New Haven, Conn.] May 13, 1828: Port of New Haven. Arrived, Brig *Shepherdess*, Ward, St. Croix, 15 days, Left at St. Croix, April 23d... brig *Union*, Ranney, discharging. *The National Advocate*, June 6, 1828: Middletown, June 4 arr brig *Union*, Rainey [*sic*], fm St. Croix. *Ibid.*, November 21, 1828: Middletown, Nov. 17. – Cl'd brig *Union*, Rainey [*sic*], St. Croix.

Unfortunately, complete issues of the various newspapers consulted were not always available. No mention of Captain Ranney's ship was discovered in the following year. However, later, on October 6, 1829, the obituary column of *The Connecticut Courant* recorded the following: "At Middletown, Mr. Thomas Eddy, 36; Capt. William Ranney, 68..." Whether this was the artist's father is not certain, but would seem likely. If so, the age is most surely incorrect, for William Ranney's father died in his forty-sixth year.

5 William Nott, Jr. (c. 1789-1840), was the only son of William Nott, Sr., and Elizabeth Duncan, of Middletown, Connecticut. He married Elizabeth Gaylord, sister of Clarissa Gaylord [Ranney], and went in 1817 to Fayetteville, North Carolina, where he was engaged in business ventures. In 1910, after the death of their son, John Josiah Nott (b. 1833), the Nott estate was settled, members of the Ranney, Gaylord, Nott and Starr families being among the heirs. See John G. Shaw, *Statement in Relation to Estate of John Nott, Late of Cumberland County, North Carolina* (Fayetteville, n.d. [c. 1910]), p. 5, "... John Nott at the time of his death owned about 2800 acres of land in Texas ... and a small amount of personal property there. He had personal property in Cumberland County, North Carolina, amounting to more than ten thousand dollars, and also owned the old Nott homestead near Fayetteville...." Claude J. Ranney has a number of letters and other data regarding this settlement, in which his father, James Joseph Ranney (son of William Ranney, the artist) was designated as one of the heirs.

6 [Margaret Ranney] "Appletons' Cyclopaedia Questionnaire," MS., New York Public Library, [c. 1883], said he "... made his first sketches at the home of his Uncle William Nott, of Raleigh [sic] N. Carolina, who adopted him after the death of his father. He had ample opportunity to indulge his love for field sports and spent much of his time in the beautiful pine woods surrounding his boyhood home."

7 In a lecture on American art given for the benefit of the Ranney sale, December 9, 1858 (see the *New-York Times*, December 10, 1858) the noted lawyer, friend and patron of the artist, James Topham Brady, stated: "... some of his pencil sketches made during his intervals from labor [in Fayetteville] attracted the attention of an artist who in 1835 invited him to New-York." In the obituary notices of William Ranney's death, both the *New-York Times*, November 24, 1857, and the *New-York Herald*, November 20, 1857, claimed that he worked for a time in an architect's office. It is difficult to ascertain what might have been the available facilities for the instruction of art in Brooklyn at this time. Augustus Graham (of the Graham Academy and the Brooklyn Institute) does not appear in the Brooklyn city directories until 1841-1842. A note in *The Knickerbocker*, July, 1856, page 29, stated: "... Two or more years since, an English gentleman, Mr. Graham, left the sum of five thousand dollars to establish a school of design in Brooklyn. A part of the interest, it was provided, should be expended annually for the purchase of a picture by an American artist, and thus a gallery instituted ...." Whether the Brooklyn Apprentices' Library Association was in existence in 1834 has not been determined, but in their advertisements in the early 1840's, drawing courses were listed along with other disciplines (see the *Brooklyn Eagle*, October 29, 1841). The New York Mechanics' Institute, where Ranney was given an award in 1838 for a painting, would have been accessible to him from the standpoint of time, for it began in 1830. Perhaps the American Academy of Arts or the National Academy of Design would have been other possibilities, but no records listing Ranney as a student are known.

8 The following items pertaining to William Ranney's service with the Texan Army are located in the Comptroller's Military Service Records, Texas State Archives, Texas State Library, Austin, Texas.

THIS CERTIFICATE

No. 990 $48.00

Entitles Wm. Ranney – to Forty Eight Dollars, for Six Months and – Days services, from Eighteenth May until Eighteenth Nov. – in Capt. Fowlers Company
1836

Geo. W. Poe

Columbia, Nov. 21st 1836   actg Paymaster General
THIS CERTIFICATE

No. 1409 $24.00

Entitles W. Ranney attory D Deaddereck to Twenty Four Dollars, for Three Months and – Day's services, from 12 March until 12 of June, in Texas Army.

Geo. W. Poe
actg Paymaster General

Columbia, Decr 1836

Received from A. Brigham, Auditor, a draft on the Treasurer in my favor, forty eight A P. Dollars – Cents in full, for the annexed instrument.

Columbia 23rd Nov. 1836
Wm. Ranney

9 The New York Mechanics' Institute might have offered a particularly strong attraction to Ranney, especially with the latter's training as a tinsmith. The relationship between the artisan and fine arts appears to have been a rather healthy one during this period. It was not

until later in the century that the separation between the two became more sharply drawn. In a *Circular of the Mechanics' Institute* (New York, 1836), pp. 2-3, the following statement of purposes was made. "It has for its object the instruction of mechanics and others in all the useful branches of science and the arts.... In accomplishing its designs, the Institute has established regular annual courses of lectures on a variety of subjects connected with improvements in the arts, but more especially, on classical and mechanical philosophy." Classes in architectural and mechanical drawing were offered. In this context, one of the more forthright statements of the relationship between the mechanic arts and the fine arts was made by a layman, the Baltimore lawyer and collector, John H. B. Latrobe, when he delivered the Annual Address before the Maryland Institute for the Promotion of the Mechanic Arts, in October, 1848. "...Let instruction in drawing, therefore, be as common as instruction in writing. Let the hand be taught the forms of grace and truth as well as pot hooks and hangers, and the pupil will not only become a better mechanic, but he will grow up to be a better man. If he learns to appreciate the beautiful on paper, he will soon find himself looking for the beautiful in Nature...." *Annual Opening and Concluding Addresses Delivered Before The Maryland Institute for the Promotion of the Mechanic Arts* (Baltimore, c. 1850). The Ranney diploma is in the collection of Claude J. Ranney (see No. 4).

[10] G. H., "Death Of William Ranney," c. 1857, unidentified clipping pasted in *The Ranney Collection* volume, New York Historical Society. "...He then returned to New York, sometime in the spring of '37, and once more applied himself to painting. After some two years of unsuccessful labor, he once more bent his steps toward Fayetteville, where he remained until the death of his uncle, when, the genius of painting, ever watching over him, once more induced him to turn his steps toward New York, the final home of his fame and of his triumphs."

[11] *The New-York City and Co-Partnership Directory for 1843 & 1844* (New York, 1843), p. 279; *The New-York City Directory for 1844 & 1845* (New York, 1844), p. 286; *New York City Directory for 1845 and 1846* (New York, 1845), p. 340.

[12] *Doggett's New-York City Directory, for 1845 and 1846* (New York, 1845), p. 298; *Ibid., for 1846 and 1847* (New York, 1846), p. 322; *Ibid., for 1847 & 1848* (New York, 1847), p. 336.

[13] Claude J. Ranney recalls an anecdote that his father, James Ranney, would recount concerning an incident which occurred when the Stevens family sent their "carriage mules" to drive Margaret Ranney and the children over to "Castle Point," the Stevens residence in Hoboken. James Ranney, then a small boy, fell off the carriage, injuring an ear on one of the wheels, and causing a scar to which he would point when telling the story.

[14] *Bulletin of the American Art-Union*, June, 1850, p. 45. "Louis Lang, A. H. Wenzler, Wm. Ranney, W. C. Boutelle, C. P. Cranch and J. R. Gifford, were elected Associates... [of the National Academy of Design]."

[15] He was born there and lived in the house until he was about twelve years old.

[16] An earlier description of the house and studio was included in *The Crayon*, January, 1858, p. 26. "...[he] removed to West Hoboken, where he built a picturesque cottage, having a large and commodious studio attached. This was so arranged as to receive animals as the objects of study, and on these occasions, with the artist at work, surrounded by all the accessories of his peculiar branch, a picture itself was afforded well worth painting. In this studio were displayed old flint-lock guns, pistols, and cutlasses, and trappings characteristic of border life, suspended from every corner; while saddles and riding gear of patterns belonging to the early history of our land, besides numerous and well-painted oil studies covered the walls, making this quiet retreat one of the most novel and interesting...." The only studio items remaining in the possession of the family are a shotgun, powder flasks, and palette and palette knife, in the collection of Claude J. Ranney. By way of comparison, an interesting note was contributed to *The Knickerbocker*, July, 1856, pp. 26-27, which advised "...Go and see the artists. They are scattered all over the metropolis: sometimes to be found in a lofty attic, at others in a hotel; here over a shop, there in a back-parlor; now in the old Dispensary, and again in the new University: isolated or in small groups, they live in their own fashion, not a few practicing rigid and ingenious economies, others nightly in 'elite' circles or at sumptuous dinners; some genially cradled in a domestic nest, and others philosophically forlorn in bacheloric solitude. But wherever found, there is a certain atmosphere of content, of independence, and of originality in their domiciles...."

[17] Charles Lanman, *Haphazard Personalities* (Boston, 1886), p. 177.

[18] *50th Anniversary of the Incorporation of the Town of West Hoboken, N. J.*, (West Hoboken, 1911), n.p.

[19] In addition to the local hunting in the New Jersey area, Ranney is said to have made an occasional trip to Canada.

[20] Claude J. Ranney pointed out that the artist kept the records for the New York Cricket Club for a time, and that they are still in existence in the New York Public Library. Accounts

of the Club's activities are included in the following newspapers: *Evening Post for the Country* [New York], August 29, 1846: New York vs. Newark, Rannie [sic] listed. *New-York Daily Tribune*, September 8, 1853: "Cricket. – New-York Club vs. St. George's Club. The return match between these Clubs came off yesterday at Hoboken . . . [the match lasted from 11:15 A.M. to 6:00 P.M.] Waller [St. George's] got a run, and then we had eight maiden ones before Blackburn got a run, and the next over he was caught well by Ranney, 1 wicket 4 runs . . ." See also *Ibid.*, September 9, 1853; *New-York Herald*, September 9, 20, 27, 1853; *New-York Daily Tribune*, September 16, 20, 27, and October 4, 1853; *New-York Herald*, June 22, October 19, 1854; *New-York Daily Tribune*, October 18, 19, 1854.

[21] Charles Collard Adams, *Middletown Upper Houses* (New York, 1908), p. 230. Clarissa Gaylord Ranney, the artist's mother, was admitted to the South Congregational Church of Middletown, Connecticut, on December 7, 1827.

[22] See the Appendix, The Ranney Fund Exhibition and Sale.

[23] The Ranney Fund sale was not without precedent. After the death of Henry Inman, on January 17, 1846, a committee of twelve was appointed at the January 20, 1846, meeting of the National Academy of Design to organize a fund-raising exhibition of his work (see *The Evening Post* [New York], January 21, 1846). The chairman of the Inman committee was Thomas S. Cummings, who undoubtedly advised the Ranney Fund group later. Judging from various contemporary accounts, the Inman exhibition was considered a success. See the *New-York Daily Tribune*, January 20, February 2, 9, 12, 23, March 10, 1846; *The Evening Post* [New York], February 11, 14, 25, 1846, and Theodore Bolton, "Henry Inman, An Account of His Life and Works," *The Art Quarterly*, Autumn, 1940, p. 372.

[24] The *Fund Catalogue* is in the volume entitled *The Ranney Collection*, New York Historical Society (see Appendix). Another copy, from the collection of Samuel P. Avery, is in the Library of the Metropolitan Museum of Art, New York. This copy also has the prices noted, but not the names of the buyers.

[25] *New-York Times*, December 10, 1858. Apparently the whole text of his speech is reproduced in this issue.

[26] According to figures cited in *The Crayon*, January, 1859, p. 27, $7,693 was given as the total; in *Ibid.*, February, 1859, p. 58, the net proceeds were recorded as $7,137.86. The *New-York Daily Tribune*, January 20, 1859, gave $7,137.80. Written on the back of the *Fund Catalogue*, New York Historical Society, the final amount was listed as $7,623.00.

[27] *New-York Daily Tribune*, January 20, 1859.

[28] *Ibid.*, at the same meeting, "the subject of the formation of an Artist's Benevolent Society was informally discussed, and a Committee, consisting of the following gentlemen, was appointed: T. S. Cummings, C. L. Elliott, T. F. Tait, T. B. Stearns, T. H. Cafferty and N. B. Collins, for the purpose of drafting a constitution and by-laws, and reporting at a future meeting to be called by them." See also *The Evening Post* [New York], January 21, 1859, and Thomas S. Cummings, *Historic Annals of the National Academy of Design* (Philadelphia, 1865), p. 266, ". . . at the earnest request of many artists, the writer drafted a plan, which embodied "THE ACTION" in the Ranney case into a society or association form, for a permanency; and likewise a code of by-laws calculated therefore, which was deemed acceptable, and a society as immediately organized, under the title of "The Artist's Fund Society of New-York."

[29] In the Ranney *Fund Catalogue*, p. 6, the painting by Church was called SOUTH AMERICAN SCENERY (No. 167). An unidentified clipping from the volume *The Ranney Collection*, called Church's painting ". . . a 'chef d'oeuvre'. . . about twelve inches by eight, was knocked down at the moderate sum of $555 . . . ."

[30] Frederick Jackson Turner, *The Frontier in American History* (New York, 1920 and 1950), pp. 1, 12.

[31] See Everett S. Lee, "The Turner Thesis Reëxamined," *American Quarterly*, Spring, 1961, pp. 77-83.

[32] The *Transactions* and *Bulletins* of the American Art-Union must be considered among our earliest significant art publications. Edited by William Hoppin, they are an invaluable source of information for the period.

[33] James Thomas Flexner, in Mary Bartlett Cowdrey, *American Academy of Fine Arts and American Art-Union* (New York, 1953), Vol. I, p. viii. For an informative summary of the art union idea and its various forms and applications, see the article in the Art-Union *Bulletin*, Sept. 1, 1851, p. 91. The Cosmopolitan Art Association, located at Sandusky, Ohio, rekindled some of the interest in art unions in the later 1850's.

CATALOGUE KEY

Title: either the original or the one by which the work is generally known. Other titles, or variations by which the work was known at different times are included in parentheses.

Arrangement of items in each section: listed in approximate chronological order. Verified dates, as e.g. in signed and dated paintings, or when there can be little question according to other sources, are given under the title. A *circa* indicates an approximation.

Medium, support, size: are listed in that order, when known. Size is indicated in inches, height by width.

Signature, initials or inscriptions: are indicated, with their approximate location on the work.

Exhibitions: arranged chronologically.

Collections: arranged chronologically. Where a question exists, an indication is made within brackets.

References: include all known recordings of the work, arranged in chronological order and numerically keyed to the bibliography. However, in the case of repetitious advertisements, only the earliest record is indicated.

Comment: includes quotations from contemporary or other sources pertaining to the work, either advancing an opinion on its merits, or lack of them, or explaining the significance of the subject. Also may include other information regarding errors, controversy, copies, comparisons, and associational material.

CATALOGUE

PART I

OIL PAINTINGS

1

SELF-PORTRAIT

present owner: Miss Margaret Ranney, Union City, New Jersey

verified date: c. 1830's

medium, support: oil on wood

size: 21½ × 16½

references:
1, pp. 293, 300

comment:
Ranney was said to have been eighteen years old when he painted this portrait,
according to family tradition. If this is correct, the date of the painting would be about 1831.

2

PORTRAIT OF CLARISSA GAYLORD RANNEY,
MOTHER OF THE ARTIST
(*The Sea Captain's Wife*)

present owner: Mr. Claude J. Ranney, Malvern, Pennsylvania

medium, support: oil on copper

size: 12½ × 10½

initialed, l.r.: « W. R. »

inscribed, on back: « W. Ranney »

collection:
Miss Margaret Ranney, Union City, New Jersey.

3

COUNTRY BRIDGE NEAR MIDDLETOWN, CONNECTICUT

present owner: Miss Margaret Ranney, Union City, New Jersey

medium: oil

size: 11½ × 9

signed: « Ranney ».

4

A COURTING SCENE

present owner: Location unknown.

verified date: c. 1838

medium: oil

exhibitions:
The Mechanics' Institute, N.Y., « Fourth Annual Fair », Sept., 1838

comment:
Mr. Claude J. Ranney, the artist's grandson,
has in his possession a diploma inscribed:
« The Mechanics' Institute Of The City Of New York / Diploma / At Their Fair Of 1838 / To William Ranny [sic] / For An Original Painting In Oil / A Courting Scene... ».

5

PORTRAIT OF MR. THOMPSON
(*35 years porter of Merchants' Bank*).

present owner: Location unknown.

verified date: c. 1838.

exhibitions:
National Academy of Design, N. Y.,
« Thirteenth Annual Exhibition, » 1838, No. 326.

collections:
Merchants' Bank, N. Y.

references:
120, i; 11, Vol. II, p. 88.

6

THE BATTLE OF COWPENS
(*Skirmish of horses, Lieut. Col. Washington in the midst of the British Dragoons, at the Battle of Cowpens*).

present owner: Dr. J. Lewi Donhauser, Loudonville, New York.

verified date: 1845.

medium, support: oil on canvas.

size: 36 × 46.

signed and dated, l.r.: « Ranney, 1845 ».

exhibitions:
National Academy of Design, N. Y.,
« Twentieth Annual Exhibition, » 1845, No. 206.

collections:
Mr. Acars Rathbun; Miss Anna French;
Mrs. J. L. Donhauser, all of Albany, N. Y.

references:
120, ii, p. 17; 162, ii, May 3; 106, v; 180;
14, p. 291; 11, Vol. II, p. 88; 132; 186;
31, pp. 320, 380; 49; 174, ii; 136.

comment:
The Battle of Cowpens took place in the northwestern section of South Carolina on January 17, 1781.
Retreating and outnumbered American forces,
under Gen. Daniel Morgan, succeeded in making a stand against the picked troops
of Col. Banastre Tarleton, completely routing them in this action. The incident portrayed by Ranney
occurred near the end of the battle,
and was described in the National Academy's *Catalogue*,
from Marshall's *Life of Washington*,
in the following manner:

> In the eagerness of pursuit,
> Washington [Lt. Col. William Washington,
> a relative of Gen. Washington, commanded
> the cavalry under Morgan] advanced nearly
> thirty yards in front of the regiment.
> Observing this, three British officers
> wheeled about and attacked him;
> the officer on his left was aiming to cut him
> down, when a serjeant came up and
> intercepted the blow by disabling his swordarm,
> at the same instant the officer on his right
> was about to make a stroke at him, when a
> waiter, too small to wield a sword, saved
> him by wounding the officer with a pistol.
> At this moment, Tarleton, made a thrust
> at him, which he parried, upon which the
> officer retreated a few paces, and discharged
> his pistol at him, which wounded him in the knee.

The name 'Cowpens' derived from the fact that there were no settlements in the immediate vicinity at that time, the area being used to pasture cattle. A contributor to the *Tribune*, November 25, 1842, who attended a celebration of the battle's anniversary in 1835, described the terrain as « ... a beautiful and almost perfect plain, with a fine surrounding growth of tall pines, oak and chestnut. » Commenting on the significance of the battle, Kenneth Roberts pointed out (1957) that the:

> ... battle destroyed the apathy of the people of
> the North, and awoke them to a realization
> of the violence of the war in the South,
> to the knowledge of the lengths to which
> the British would go to separate the South
> from the North and retain it as a British Colony,
> to the certainty that even the best of British
> leaders could be overwelmingly defeated,
> and to the necessity of supplying their pitiful ghost
> army in the South with the troops and supplies
> that eventually made it possible for Cornwallis
> to be cornered at Yorktown...

A grateful Continental Congress awarded the rough Gen. Morgan a gold plaque, designed by the French artist, Augustin Dupré, as a token of his deed.

7

RADISH GIRL
present owner: Location unknown
verified date: c. 1845
exhibitions:
National Academy of Design, N. Y.,
« Twentieth Annual Exhibition, » 1845, No. 56
collection:
Mr. Charles L. Vose
references:
120, ii, p. 11; 162, i; 11, Vol. II, p. 88
comment:
An unsympathetic criticism of this work appeared in the *Herald* review of the Academy exhibition. At the Ranney Fund Sale in 1858, a painting entitled « Raddish [sic?] Girl » was sold to "Hurlbut" for eleven dollars (*Fund Catalogue*, No. 154).

8

THE WOUNDED TROOPER
present owner: Location unknown
verified date: c. 1845
exhibitions:
American Art-Union, N. Y., 1845, No 35
collections:
American Art-Union, N. Y.; Mr. James S. Davis, N. Y.
references:
71, i, p. 27; 10, Vol. II, p. 294.

9

MARINE VIEW
present owner: Location unknown
verified date: c. 1845
exhibitions:
American Art-Union, N. Y., 1845, No. 97

collections:
American Art-Union, N. Y.; Mr. George E. Cook, N. Y.
references:
71, i, p. 29; 10, Vol. II, p. 294.

10

DEER HUNTERS
present owner: Location unknown
verified date: c. 1845
size: c. 20×25
signed and dated, l. l.: « [W] Ranney 184 [5 ?]. »

11

THE MATCH BOY
(*The Match Seller*)
present owner: Francis S. Grubar, Washington, D. C.
verified date: 1845
size: 30×25
signed, l. c., on box: « Ranney 1845 »
inscribed on top of box: « Boxes » and above the signature, « Matches. »
inscribed in ink on label pasted to stretcher on reverse: « R. A. McDonald / Christmas 1904 / Jessie & Ralph Dunn. »
exhibitions:
National Academy of Design, N. Y.,
« Twenty-First Annual Exhibition, » 1846, No. 192
collections:
Mr. Charles L. Vose; Jessie & Ralph Dunn [?]; R. A. McDonald; Dr. Sidney Ulfelder & Mrs. Ethel M. Ulfelder, « Maplewood Estate, » McLean, Va.
references:
120, iii, p. 17; 106, iii; 11, Vol. II, p. 88
comment:
The Knickerbocker, June, 1846, in discussing the National Academy Exhibition, mentioned that « ... Mr. Ranney is a young artist who is steadily improving. His 'Match-Boy,' No. 192, is a very good thing indeed... ».

12

COAST SCENE WITH FIGURES
present owner: Location unknown
verified date: c. 1846
exhibitions:
American Art-Union, N. Y., 1846, No. 20
collections:
American Art-Union, N. Y.; Mr. Robert Ray, N. Y.
references:
71, ii, p. 31; 172, vii; 161, iv; 10, Vol. II, p. 294.

13

THE DEAD COURSER
present owner: Location unknown
verified date: c. 1846
exhibitions:
National Academy of Design, N. Y.,
« Twenty-First Annual Exhibition, » 1846, No. 54
references:
120, iii, p. 11; 172, vi; 11, Vol. II, p. 88

comment:

The *Tribune* article stated: « This is a small picture
by Ranney, and is hung in a low and unfavorable position.
But it is a powerful and startling piece, and will hold
a higher place in your memory than
on the Gallery walls. »

14

THE DEAD CHARGER
present owner: Location unknown
verified date: c. 1846
exhibitions:
American Art-Union, N. Y., 1846, No. 31
collections:
American Art-Union, N. Y.; D. A. Wood, N. Y.
references:
161, iv; 10, Vol. II, p. 294
comment:

It would appear likely that this painting
and THE DEAD COURSER (No. 13) were the same.
No purchaser was listed for the latter
at the National Academy exhibition held earlier that year.
As the number of subscribers to the Art-Union grew,
so did that organization's need for distribution paintings.
In spite of some friction between the two groups,
it became the policy of the Art-Union to acquire
increasing numbers of paintings from the Academy shows.
See the catalogue appended to the Art-Union *Bulletin*,
June 1, 1847, and other issues. An asterisk was used
to denote those paintings purchased by the Art-Union
but still hanging in the current National Academy
Annual Exhibition.

15

CROSSING THE FERRY – SCENE ON THE PEDEE
(*The Crossing*)
present owner: Location unknown
verified date: c. 1846
medium, support: oil on canvas
size: 28×42
signed, on boat: « Ranney »
exhibitions:
National Academy of Design, N. Y.,
« Twenty-First Annual Exhibition, » 1846, No. 304;
American Art-Union, N. Y., 1846, No. 30
collections:
American Art-Union, N. Y.; A. M. L. Scott, N. Y.;
Mr. A. E. Douglass, N. Y.; Private Collection, Conn.;
with David B. Findlay Galleries, N. Y.
references:
120, iii, p. 22; 71, ii, p. 31; 172, vii; 161, iv;
92, v; 11, Vol. II, p. 88; 10, Vol. II, p. 294; 78, vi.
comment:

From *The Crayon* for May, 1857:
« The collection of pictures belonging to A. E. Douglass,
Esq., lately disposed of at auction, indicates a growing
taste for Art in this community... A picture by Ranney,
called « The Crossing, » brought $122... ».

16

JACK
present owner: Location unknown
verified date: c. 1846
exhibitions:
National Academy of Design, N. Y.,
« Twenty-First Annual Exhibition, » 1846, No. 20
references:
120, iii, p. 10; 11, Vol. II, p. 88.

17

FRIENDSHIP IN ADVERSITY
present owner: Location unknown
verified date: c. 1846
exhibitions:
National Academy of Design, N. Y.,
« Twenty-First Annual Exhibition, » 1846, No. 332.
references:
120, iii, p. 23; 11, Vol. II, p. 88.

18

SHAD FISHING ON THE HUDSON
present owner: Location unknown
verified date: c. 1846
exhibitions:
American Art-Union, N. Y., 1846, No. 44
collections:
American Art-Union, N. Y.; Mr. David T. Valentine, N. Y.
references:
71, ii, p. 31; 10, Vol. II, p. 294.

19

COAST SCENE, WITH FISHERMEN
present owner: Location unknown
verified date: c. 1846
exhibitions:
American Art-Union, N. Y., 1846, No. 121
collections:
American Art-Union, N. Y.; J. H. Obear, Macon, Ga.
references:
71, ii, p. 34; 10, Vol. II, p. 294.

20

THE LASSO
present owner: Mr. Claude J. Ranney,
Malvern, Pennsylvania
verified date: 1896
medium, support: oil on canvas
size: 31×42
signed and dated, l. l.: « Ranney / 1846 »
exhibitions:
Denver Art Museum, Denver, Col.,
« Building the West, » Oct., 1956, No. 73
collections:
Mr. James Harold Frazer; Mrs. J. H. Crenshaw,
Front Royal, Va.; Mr. T. Gilbert Brouillette,
Falmouth, Mass.

references:

93, pp. 25, 30

comment:

From Geo. Catlin, *Letters and Notes on the Manners, Customs, and Condition of the North American Indians,* 1841, Vol. II, page 58:

> The usual mode of taking the wild
> horses, is, by throwing the 'laso,'
> whilst pursuing them at full speed,
> and dropping a noose over their necks,
> by which their speed is soon checked,
> and they are 'choked down.' The 'laso'
> is a thong of raw hide, some ten or
> fifteen yards in length, twisted or
> braided, with a noose fixed at the
> end of it; which, when the coil of
> the 'laso' is thrown out, drops with
> great certainty over the neck of the
> animal, which is soon conquered.

21

HUNTING WILD HORSES

(*Wild Horses; Catching Wild Horses; Wild Horse on the Prairie; The Lasso*)
present owner: M. Knoedler and Company, New York
verified date: 1846
medium, support: oil on canvas
size: 36×54½
signed and dated, l. l.: « Ranney / 1846 »

exhibitions:

U. S. Sanitary Commission, « Great Central Fair, » Philadelphia, June, 1864, No. 213;
M. Knoedler and Company, N. Y., « The Far West, » Feb. 7-26, 1949; Joslyn Art Museum, Omaha, Neb., « Life on the Prairie, » May 12-July 4, 1954; Canadian National Exhibition, Aug. 27-Sept. 11, 1954, No. 124; City Art Museum of St. Louis, « Westward the Way, » Oct. 22-Dec. 6, 1954, No. 123 [as THE LASSO]; Walker Art Center, Minneapolis, « Westward the Way, » Jan. 4-Feb. 28, 1955, No. 123 [as THE LASSO]; William Rockhill Nelson Gallery... and Mary Atkins Museum of Fine Arts, Kansas City, Mo., « The Last Frontier, » Oct. 5-Nov. 17, 1957, No. 48

collections:

Mr. Marshall O. Roberts, N. Y.;
Mrs. Marshall O. Roberts, N. Y.

references:

92, iv; 137, p. 10; 58, pp. 431, 626; 54, Vol. II, p. 16 [as THE LASSO]; 95, p. 49, No. 152; 172, xxxi; 97; 17, p. 377; 104 [as THE LASSO]; 131, pp. 158, 267, jacket [as THE LASSO]; 144, p. 10.

comment:

The confusion which has arisen concerning the title of this work and No. 20 may be traced back to Strahan [Earl Shinn] in c. 1880, when the title THE LASSO appeared in the section of the book devoted to the Roberts collection.
Earlier references invariably called it HUNTING [or CATCHING] WILD HORSES or WILD HORSE ON THE PRAIRIE. By the time the Roberts Estate sale occurred in 1897, American artistic taste had shifted considerably from that of the first half of the century, and prices received were generally low.
Although this painting was sold for seventy dollars, some measure of the ability of Ranney's work to maintain a certain stature among that of his contemporaries is indicated by the fact that a large painting by Durand brought only eighty-five dollars.

> The wild horse of these regions is a small,
> but very powerful animal;
> with an exceedingly prominent eye, sharp nose,
> high nostril, small feet and delicate leg....
> Catlin, *Ibid.*, p. 57.

22

THE PENNSYLVANIA TEAMSTER

(*Going to the Mill; Carting Flour; Hauling Flour*)
present owner: Thomas Gilcrease Institute of American History and Art, Tulsa, Oklahoma
verified date: 1846
medium, support: oil on canvas
size: 29½×40
signed, on rock, l. r.: « Ranney / 1846 »

exhibitions:

American Art-Union, N. Y., 1847, No. 4; Lyman Allyn Museum, New London, Conn., « Eighty Eminent Painters of Connecticut, » Mar. 9-Apr. 20, 1947, No. 66.

collections:

American Art-Union, N. Y.; J. J. Haines, N. Y.; Kennedy Galleries, N. Y.

references:

71, iii, p. 32; 69, i, ii, p. 8; 110, iii; 69, iii, p. 6, iv, 5; 112; 111, No. 66; 10, Vol. II, p. 294.

comment:

The Literary World, October 23, 1847, in a review of the American Art-Union pictures on display for that year's distribution, stated: « There is a deal of bad drawing.... The teamster appears to have but one leg, and there is very little indication that he is sitting on the back of his horse.
The picture, however, is free and spirited. »

23

THE EAGLE'S NEST

present owner: Location unknown
verified date: c. 1847

exhibitions:

American Art-Union, N. Y., 1847, No. 19

collections:

American Art-Union, N. Y.; A. B. Matthews, Pontiac, Mich.

references:

71, iii, p. 33; 69, i, ii, p. 8; 110, iii; 69, iii, p. 6, iv, p. 5; 10, Vol. II, p. 294.

comment:

The same review, quoted in No. 22 from *The Literary World*, also mentions this painting as being free and spirited
« ... though the rocks are artificially arranged. »

WASHINGTON'S MISSION TO THE INDIANS IN 1753
(*Washington on his Mission to the Indians*)
present owner: Location unknown
verified date: c. 1847
exhibitions:

National Academy of Design, N. Y.,
« Twenty-Second Annual Exhibition, » 1847, No. 88;
American Art-Union, N. Y., 1847, No. 30

collections:

American Art-Union, N. Y.; A. G. Carll, Jericho, N. Y.

references:

120, iv, p. 13; 71, iii, p. 33; 110, i; 69, i, ii, p. 9;
110, iii; 69, iii, p. 7, iv, p. 6; 181; 63, p. 181;
27, p. 772; 28, p. 549; 17, p. 377; 11, Vol. II,
p. 88; 10, Vol. II, p. 294.

comment:

For a brief summary of the historical setting for this theme,
see the commentary under No. 81. The Art-Union
publications for 1847 included the following
quotation from Headley:

> For 750 miles, more than half the distance
> through an unbroken wilderness, accompanied
> by only seven persons, across rivers, and
> morasses, over mountains, through fearful
> gorges, and amidst tribes of Indians, the
> fearless stripling pursued his way for
> forty-one days.

A lengthy article in *The Literary World* for March 27,
1847, gave the following description:

> ... The picture represents the party
> struggling over the mountains through
> a blinding snowstorm....

Ranney's WASHINGTON AND GIST CROSSING
THE ALLEGHENY RIVER, No. 81, portrays another
episode of Washington's mission.

25

SLEIGHING

present owner: Mr. and Mrs. J. Maxwell Moran,
Paoli, Pennsylvania
verified date: c. 1847
medium, support: oil on canvas
size: 30 × 42
signed, l. c.: « Ranney »
exhibitions:

National Academy of Design, N. Y.,
« Twenty-Second Annual Exhibition, » 1847, No. 305;
M. Knoedler and Company, N. Y.,
« The Far West, » 1949.

collections:

McClees Galleries, Philadelphia;
Mr. Claude J. Ranney, Malvern, Pa.

references:

120, iv, p. 21; 110, ii; 181; 11, Vol. II, p. 88

comment:

The Literary World, June 12, 1847, assumed a rather
carping attitude, when it stated that this work
« ... is spirited, but badly drawn.
The dog looks like a fish's vertebra... ».

FIRST NEWS OF THE BATTLE OF LEXINGTON
present owner: The North Carolina Museum of Art,
Raleigh, North Carolina
verified date: 1847
medium, support: oil on canvas
size: 44 × 63
signed and dated, on door, l. l.: « Ranney / 1847 »
exhibitions:

American Art-Union, N. Y., 1847, No. 149;
John Nicholson Gallery, N. Y., Sept., 1947;
Robert C. Vose Galleries, Boston, « American Landscape
and Figure Painters, » Summer, 1948, No. 24.

collections:

American Art-Union, N. Y.; Mrs. J. S. Cogdell,
Charleston, S. C.; John Nicholson Gallery, N. Y.

references:

71, iii, p. 39; 110, iii; 69, iii, p. 11; 110, iv;
69, iv, p. 10; 82, iii; 103; 79, vi, p. 17; 140, i, ii, No. 24;
10, Vol. II, p. 294; 125, No. 29

comment:

The Art-Union publications for 1847 gave the following
description for this painting:

> The tidings spread – men galloped
> from town to town beating the drum
> and calling to arms. The people
> snatched their rifles and fowling
> pieces, and hurried towards Boston.
> The voice of war rang through the land,
> and preparations were every where
> commenced for united action.

The Literary World for October 23, 1847,
in the same review referred to in Nos. 22 and 24,
expressed dissatisfaction with what was considered
to be Ranney's lack of progress as an artist.
« ... Every new picture by a young artist should
show a long step in advance; but his last picture,
now at the Art-Union rooms, 'The news of the battle
of Lexington,' is not so meritorious as...
'Washington's Mission to the Indians,' exhibited
at the Academy... ».

27

BURIAL OF DE SOTO
present owner: Location unknown
verified date: c. 1847
exhibitions:

American Art-Union, N. Y., 1847, No. 264.

collections:

American Art-Union, N. Y.; Mr. George T. Plume, N. Y.

references:

71, iii, p. 43; 58, p. 431; 41, p. 411 [?]; 97; 52, p. 240;
17, p. 377; 85, i, p. 462; 174, i [?]; 10, Vol. II, p. 294;
119 [?]

comment:

Until the original painting is located, or at least
a contemporary description of it discovered,
some question must remain whether several sources
cited above, marked with a question,
are actually illustrations from Ranney's unlocated picture.

WASHINGTON RALLYING THE AMERICANS
AT THE BATTLE OF PRINCETON

(*George Washington in the Battle of Princeton*;
*Washington Rallying the Americans at the Battle
of Princeton, After the Death of Gen. Mercer*)
present owner: Prospect Hall, Princeton University,
Princeton, New Jersey
verified date: 1848
medium, support: oil on canvas
size: 48½×64
signed and dated, l. c.: « W. Ranney / 1848, »
and *l. r.*: « Henry Inman, 1834 »

exhibitions:

National Academy of Design, N. Y.,
« Twenty-Third Annual Exhibition, » 1848, No. 177

collections:

Manigault Collection, Charleston, S. C.;
Mr. Edward Wassermann, N. Y.; Corcoran Gallery of Art,
Washington, D. C.

references:

120, v, p. 16; 177, iv, ii [as by Inman];
11, Vol. II, p. 88; 114; 18, p. 329, Fig. 223;
78, iii; 133.

comment:

The painting was considered to be by Inman until 1920,
when it underwent restoration and the Ranney
signature appeared. It was presented
to the Princeton University Art Museum in 1911
by the consent of Mr. Edward Wassermann,
on behalf of his children.
If the signatures and dates on this painting
are authentic, it would seem reasonable to suggest
that Ranney might have finished a work begun
by Inman, who died in 1846. After the death of Ranney
in the next decade, several of his paintings were
completed by other artists. See Nos. 85, 92, 93 and 94.

29

VETERANS OF 1776 RETURNING FROM THE WAR

(*Revolutionary Hero's Return*; *American Revolutionary
Hero's Return*; *Return of Revolutionary Veterans*)
present owner: Location unknown
verified date: c. 1848

exhibitions:

American Art-Union, N. Y., 1848, No. 110;
Pennsylvania Academy of Fine Arts, Philadelphia,
« Twenty-Eighth Annual Exhibition, » 1851, No. 169;
U. S. Sanitary Commission, « Great Central Fair, »
Philadelphia, June, 1864, No. 134;
Pennsylvania Academy of Fine Arts, Philadelphia, 1865,
No. 606, and 1866, No. 516.

collections:

American Art-Union, N. Y.; Mr. William E. Remsen,
Syosset, N. Y.; Mr. Harrison Earl, Philadelphia;
Mr. Henry Paul Beck, Philadelphia.

references:

69, v, vi, vii, viii, ix, x, xi, xii,
xiii, xiv; 173; 164, i; 69, xv, xvi, p. 10,
xvii, p. 11; 71, iv, p. 57; 127; 137, p. 8; 10, Vol. II,
p. 294; 50, pp. 177, 295, 311.

comment:

The painting was described in the Art-Union *Bulletin* as:

... a very merry picture. The old soldiers
are going home in a very dilapidated condition.
Their equipage is a rude cart drawn by a ruder steed.
One of the occupants is doing a grotesque dance.
The worthy who acts as postillion is looking back
in delight.... In the distance other stragglers
are dimly seen.

The *New-York Weekly Evening Post*, November 16, 1848,
began its notice of the painting with « Mr. Ranney
contributes a composition in his own peculiar line
of subjects – a line in which he rarely fails of success... ».

30

PRAIRIE BURIAL

(*American Pioneer Life – A Frontier Burial*)
present owner: Mr. and Mrs. J. Maxwell Moran,
Paoli, Pennsylvania
verified date: 1848
medium, support: oil on canvas
size: 28½×41
signed and dated, on dirt pile, l. c.: « Ranney / 1848 »

exhibitions:

American Art-Union, N. Y., 1848, No. 328;
Harry Shaw Newman Gallery, N. Y., Oct., 1945;
Lyman Allyn Museum, New London, Conn.,
« Eighty Eminent Painters of Connecticut, »
Mar. 9-April 20, 1947, No. 65; City Art Museum
of St. Louis, « Westward the Way, » Oct. 22-Dec. 6, 1954,
No. 143; Walker Art Center, Minneapolis,
« Westward the Way, » Jan. 4-Feb. 28, 1955, No. 143

collections:

American Art-Union, N. Y.; Mr. Charles De Kay,
Geneva, N. Y.; Harry Shaw Newman Gallery, N. Y.;
Mr. Claude J. Ranney, Malvern, Pa.

references:

69, xvi, p. 15, xvii, p. 20; 71 iv, p. 68; 101, i;
111, No. 65; 10, Vol. II, p. 294; 131, pp. 180, 268; 176.

comment:

From Francis Parkman, Jr., *The California
and Oregon Trail*, 1849:

These were the first emigrants we had
overtaken, although we had found abundant
and melancholy traces of their progress
throughout the course of the journey.
Sometimes we had passed the grave of one
who had sickened and died on the way....

31

PRAIRIE BURIAL

present owner: Mr. T. Gilbert Brouillette,
Falmouth, Massachusetts
medium, support: oil on canvas
size: 14×20
initialed on dirt pile, l. c.: « W R »
inscribed on the frame: « Ogden » and « 20778-97 »
exhibitions:
Mint Museum of Art, Charlotte, N. C.,
« Selected Paintings, » Oct. 1-30, 1957.

collections:

T. H. Ogden, Brooklyn, N. Y.; Mr. John J. Bowden,
Long Island, N. Y.

references:

118.

comment:

An oil study for the large painting
of the same title (No. 30).

32

THE PRAIRIE FIRE

present owner: Mr. and Mrs. J. Maxwell Moran,
Paoli, Pennsylvania
verified date: 1848
medium, support: oil on canvas
size: 38×60
signed and dated, l. c.: « Ranney / 1848 »

exhibitions:

M. Knoedler and Co., N. Y.,
« The Far West, » Feb. 7-26, 1949, No. 38;
City Art Museum of St. Louis, « Westward the Way, »
Oct. 22-Dec. 6, 1954, No. 142; Walker Art Center,
Minneapolis, « Westward the Way, » Jan. 4-Feb. 28, 1955,
No. 142; William Rockhill Nelson Gallery
and Mary Atkins Museum of Fine Arts, Kansas City, Mo.,
« The Last Frontier, » Oct. 5-Nov. 17, 1957, No. 47.

collections:

Mr. Louis Hasbrouck, N. Y.;
Knoedler Galleries, N. Y.; Mr. Claude J. Ranney,
Malvern, Pa.

references:

107; 109, i, p. 42; 38, pp. 128, 131; 131, pp. 179,
268; 144, p. 10.

comment:

George Catlin, another famous artist
of the Western scene, presents a vivid verbal
description of a similar event
in his *Letters and Notes on the Manners, Customs,
and Condition of the North American Indians*, 1841,
Vol. II, p. 18.

> But who has seen the vivid lightnings,
> and heard the roaring thunder of the
> rolling conflagration which sweeps
> over the « deep-clad » prairies of the West?
> Who has dashed, on his wild horse,
> through an ocean of grass, with the raging tempest
> at his back, rolling over the land its
> swelling waves of liquid fire?

33

STAMPEDE

present owner: Location unknown
verified date: c. 1848

exhibitions:

American Art-Union, N. Y., 1848, No. 339.

collections:

American Art-Union, N. Y.; Mr. Jacob G. Bedell,
Coxsackie, N. Y.

references:

69, xvi, p. 15, xvii, p. 20; 71, iv, p. 68;
10, Vol. II, p. 294.

34

THE FLIGHT ON THE PRAIRIE

(*Flights, Groups, Horses, & c.*)
present owner: Location unknown

collections:

Mr. J. M. Burt.

references:

167, ii; 162, xxiv; 172,
xxv, Nov. 2; 92, vi

comment:

Whether this painting and No. 33
are the same as THE PRAIRIE FIRE (No. 32)
is uncertain. According to *The Crayon* article
« ... "The Flight on the Prairie" by W. Ranney,
brought $30... » at the auction of Mr. Burt's collection.

35

FISHER BOY

present owner: Location unknown
verified date: c. 1848

exhibitions:

American Art-Union, N. Y., 1848, No. 408

collections:

American Art-Union, N. Y.; B. Blakeman, Albany, N. Y.

references:

69, xvii, p. 23; 71, iv, p. 72; 10, Vol. II, p. 294.

36

DUCK SHOOTERS

(*Duck Shooting on Penhorn Creek;
Duck Shooters on the Hoboken Marshes;
Duck Hunters; Duck Hunters on the Hoboken Marshes*)
present owner: Museum of Fine Arts, Boston,
M. and M. Karolik Collection
verified date: 1849
medium, support: oil on canvas
size: 26×40
signed and dated on side of boat: « W. Ranney / 49 »

exhibitions:

American Art-Union, N. Y., 1849, No. 13;
Museum of Fine Arts, Boston, « American Paintings,
1815-1865, » 1957-59, No. 130

collections:

American Art-Union, N. Y.; A. L. Hatch, Brooklyn, N. Y.;
Mr. Milton Rathbun, Mt. Vernon, N. Y.;
Mr. Alan Rathbun, N. Y.; Mr. T. Gilbert Brouillette,
Falmouth, Mass.; John Levy Galleries, N. Y.

references:

166, i; 110, v; 69, xviii, xix,
xxii, p. 31; 166, ii; 172, viii; 69, xxiii,
xxiv, p. 28, xxv, p. 30,
xxvi, p. 27; 70, i, p. 5, ii, p. 2;
172, ix, Dec. 22; 159, i, Dec. 22;
71, v, p. 41; 85, i; 79, vii; 80;
10, Vol. II, p. 294; 74; 85, ii

comment:

The *Morning Courier and New York Enquirer* critic,
March 28, 1849, praised this work highly,

calling it one "of the most successful
pictures on the walls."
The dimensions given for the painting
at that time were 26×46.
The view is of Penhorn Creek with the silhouette
of the still existent St. Michael's Monastery
visible at the right.
The man paddling the boat was said to have been
Nat McIver, who worked in a stable near Ranney's
studio and was a friend of the artist.

37

A RABBIT HUNTER

present owner: Location unknown
verified date: c. 1849
size: c. 22×27

exhibitions:

American Art-Union, N.Y., No. 142

collections:

American Art-Union, N.Y.; Mr. William Waters,
Franklin, N.Y.

references:

69, xxi; 166, ii; 172, viii; 70, i, p. 9, ii, p. 10;
172, ix, Dec. 22; 159, i, Dec. 22;
71, v, p. 46; 10, Vol. II, p. 294

comment:

Described in contemporary accounts
as « a hunter going through the snow with his dog
and gun. » The *Tribune*, December 22, 1849, listed
the recipient in the Art-Union drawing
as « William Wallace, Franklin, Delaware Co., N.Y. »

38

BOONE'S FIRST VIEW OF KENTUCKY

(*Daniel Boone and his companions discovering Kentucky;
Boone's discovery of Kentucky; Daniel Boone's first view
of Kentucky; The encampment of Boone;
Boone's first sight of Kentucky from the Cumberland
Mountains*)
present owner: Private Collection
verified date: 1849
medium, support: oil on canvas
size: 36×54
signed, on rock, l. r.: « W. Ranney / 1849 »

exhibitions:

American Art-Union, N.Y., 1850, No. 2;
William Rockhill Nelson Gallery of Art and The Mary
Atkins Museum of Fine Arts, Kansas City, Mo.,
« The Last Frontier, » Oct. 5-17, 1957, No. 44.

collections:

American Art-Union, N.Y.; Mrs. John Dillon,
Zanesville, Ohio; [Private Collection, Phoenix, Ariz.,
and Calif.?]; Kennedy Galleries, N.Y.

references:

69, xxii, p. 29; 110, vi; 69, xxv, p. 18, xxvii, p. 25
xxviii, facing p. 17; 162, vi; 149;
172, xv, Dec. 16; 162, vii, Dec. 17, 21; 159, ii, Dec. 18, 21;
172, xv, Dec. 21; 69, xxxvi, p. 167,
xlv, p. 8; 70, iii, p. 15; 162, xii, Dec. 18;
43, facing p. 49; 180; 14, p. 29; 58, p. 431;

181; 63, p. 181; 27, p. 772; 76; 28, p. 549;
97; 52, p. 240; 17, p. 377; 85, i, p. 462;
10, Vol. I, p. 259, Vol. II, pp. 294, 295; 144, p. 10.

comment:

With an increasing interest being generated
in the West during the early nineteenth century,
the character and exploits of a personality such
as Daniel Boone (1735-1820) assumed heroic
proportions – a kind of democratic homespun
equivalent of a Ulysses-Hercules type.
Accounts of his activities appeared frequently
in the publications of the day, and his appeal
to the artists of Ranney's generation would be obvious.
Ranney's costume portrayal of Boone and his party
coincides almost exactly with the description
of hunters found on page 23 in Peck's
Life of Daniel Boone, 1847.

> ... Their dress was of the description
> usually worn at that period by all forest
> rangers. The outside garment was a hunting
> shirt, or loose, open frock, made of dressed
> deer skins. Leggins or drawers,
> of the same material, covered the lower
> extremities, to which was appended a pair
> of moccasins for the feet. The cape or
> collar of the hunting shirt, and the seams
> of the leggins were adorned with fringes.
> The undergarments were of coarse cotton.
> A leathern belt encircled the body; on
> the right side was suspended the tomahawk,
> to be used as a hatchet; on the left side
> was the hunting-knife, powder-horn,
> bullet-pouch, and other appendages indispensable
> for a hunter. Each person bore his
> trusty rifle....

Boone's later biographer, Timothy Flint,
described the event in his *Biographical
Memoir of Daniel Boone*, 1833.

> The last crags and cliffs of the middle
> ridges had been scrambled over... they
> stood on the summit of Cumberland
> mountain, the farthest western spur
> of this line of heights.... What a scene
> opened before them! A feeling
> of the sublime is inspired in every
> bosom susceptible of it, by a view
> from any point of these vast ranges,
> of the boundless forest valleys of
> the Ohio.... From an eminence...
> they could see, as far as vision
> could extend, the beautiful country
> of Kentucky. They remarked with astonishment
> the tall, straight trees, shading
> the exuberant soil, wholly clear from
> any other underbrush than the rich
> cane-brakes, the image of verdure and
> luxuriance, or tall grass and clover.
> Down the gentle slopes murmured clear
> limestone brook. Finley [sic]... exclaimed...
> « This wilderness blossoms as the rose;
> and these desolate places are as the
> garden of God. »

Other than the literary sources of inspiration,
Ranney may well have been influenced by a rather
crude woodcut, perhaps by William Woodruff,
found on page 42 of Flint's book.
By comparison, Ranney's interpretation
is obviously a more polished performance,

but the general arrangement and iconography
found in the earlier work could have been
the point of departure for Ranney's conception,
or at least been known to him.
It would seem reasonable to suggest that Ranney's
interpretation, in turn, was the inspiration
for the wood engraving by Orr of this theme,
which appeared in Bogart's book on Boone
(1854 and subsequent editions, see No. 196).
Ranney was said to have sold the copyright
for an engraving after the Art-Union
painting to a textbook publisher.
Contemporary opinion of this work was
generally favorable; some considered it his
best effort at that time.
For those who could not see the painting
at the Art-Union Gallery in New York,
that organization published an engraving (8 × 5½)
after the painting, executed by Alfred Jones,
in the *Bulletin* for May, 1850 (No. 195). The plate
was purchased, along with others,
by Mr. Appleton at the 1852 auction
sale of the American Art-Union, which was already
embroiled in the legal contest that eventually caused
its collapse, and published several years later
in the *Ornaments of Memory* gift albums
of 1856 and 1857.
It was not unusual for Ranney to paint more
than one version of his more successful pictures.
Another BOONE'S FIRST VIEW OF KENTUCKY had been
known for some time and, until the discovery
of the painting under discussion (No. 38)
it was plausible to once believe that that was
the Art-Union painting. However, upon comparing
No. 38 with the engraving by Jones (No. 195)
and with the second version (No. 39),
there can be little doubt that No. 38 was the work
purchased and distributed by the American Art-Union.
The arrangement of the figures, rocky background
with a shattered tree on the right, the open sky
with the impression of a great height,
the treatment of the foreground with an almost
exact duplication of various small objects,
are unquestionable evidence that this painting
was the source of the Art-Union engraving,
and therefore, the original painting
acquired by that organization.
See the drawing, No. 115.
A STUDY FOR LARGE PICTURE, DANIEL BOONE AND PARTY
was purchased by « Walker » for six dollars
at the Ranney Fund sale in 1858.
(*Fund Catalogue*, No. 176).

39

BOONE'S FIRST VIEW OF KENTUCKY

present owner: M. Knoedler and Company,
New York
verified date: 1849
medium, support: oil on canvas
size: 37½ × 54
signed and dated, l. r.: « W. Ranney / 1849 »
exhibitions:
Knoedler Galleries, N. Y., « Portrait of the Old West, »
Oct. 20-Nov. 1, 1952, No. 27; Junior Art Gallery,

Louisville Free Public Library, Louisville, Ky.,
« The Wild West, » July, 1953.
collection:
Mrs. J. Madden, Greenwich, Conn.
comment:
Probably painted shortly after the American Art-Union
version (No. 38). Compositional changes
in the arrangement of the center group,
details in the foreground and background areas,
and a general softening of brushwork throughout,
produced a more sophisticated effect and harmonious,
integrated design, but at the expense of the vigor
and power expressed in the Art-Union picture.
See the drawing, No. 115.

40

TRAPPERS ON THE LOOKOUT

present owner: Location unknown
medium, support: oil on academy board
size: 8 × 10
initialed on rocks, l. r.: « W. R. »
exhibitions:
National Academy of Design, N. Y.,
« Paintings to be Sold for the Benefit of the Ranney
Fund, » Dec., 1858, No. 56.
collections: Walker; Mortimer Brandt Galleries, N. Y.
references:
180, p. 2.
comment:
Described as two frontier scouts costumed
in buckskins and fur caps, carrying long-barreled
Kentucky rifles, and wearing shoulder packs.
Two black and tan foxhounds, leashed together,
stand immediately in front of the scouts.
The scouts are apparently watching from a rocky
mountainous peak. The two figures and the hounds
are said to be almost identical with those
in the group in BOONE'S FIRST VIEW OF KENTUCKY
(Nos. 38-39). On the reverse of the academy
board is the stamp, « Müller-Paris, » and a small,
shieldlike label with the number « 56 » inscribed
therein, which corresponds to the Ranney Fund
Sale number.

41

THE TRAPPER'S LAST SHOT

(*The trapper's last bullet*)
present owner: Location unknown
verified date: c. 1850
exhibitions:
Western Art-Union, Cincinnati, 1850, No. 68
collections:
Western Art-Union, Cincinnati; Mrs. C. E. Lindley,
Indianapolis
references:
69, xxviii, p. 29, xxxiv, p. 138; 143;
148; 180; 2, p. 20; 181; 60, 1912, p. 87;
145, i; 101, ii, p. 68

comment:
A steel line engraving ($18 \times 23\frac{1}{2}$)
was executed after the painting by T. Dwight Booth
of Cincinnati, and published by J. M. Emerson
and Company, New York, for the distribution print
of the Western Art-Union in 1850 (No. 197).
Inscribed on the saddle is: « W. Ranney - 50. »

42

THE TRAPPER'S LAST SHOT

(*The last shot*; *The trapper's last bullet*;
The last bullet)
present owner: Mr. C. R. Smith,
New York
verified date: c. 1850
medium, support: oil on canvas
size: $28\frac{1}{2} \times 36$
signed, on saddle: « W. Ranney »
American Art-Union label on reverse

exhibitions:

American Art-Union, N. Y., 1850, No. 91;
Harry Shaw Newman Gallery, N. Y.,
« Nineteenth Century Painting on America, »
Oct., 1947; *Idem.*, « Sport in the Nineteenth Century, »
Feb., 1948, No. 8; Edward Eberstadt & Sons, N. Y.,
« A Distinguished Collection of Western Paintings, »
c. 1956, No. 95

collections:

American Art-Union, N. Y.; Miss Anna E. Lambert, N. Y.;
Old Print Shop, N. Y.; Peikin Galleries, N. Y.;
Edward Eberstadt & Sons, N. Y.

references:

69, xxvii, p. 15; 172, x; 110, vii;
162, vi; 69, xxxiv, p. 138; 164, iv; 172, xv, Dec. 16;
162, vii, Dec. 17, 21; 159, ii, Dec. 18, 21;
172, xv, Dec. 21; 69, xxxvi,
p. 169; 14, p. 291; 58, p. 432; 63, p. 181;
76; 97; 79, vi, p. 2; 81; 101, ii; 33, p. 215;
10, Vol. II, p. 295; 79, viii; 94.

comment:

It appears likely that Ranney painted
THE TRAPPER'S LAST SHOT at least twice in 1850,
and that one painting was distributed
by the Western Art-Union of Cincinnati, and the other
by the American Art-Union in New York.
Although the Western Art-Union version (No. 41)
has not been located, a comparison of the well-executed
Booth engraving (No. 197) with the American Art-Union
painting reveals minor differences in some of the details,
notably in the horses' tails and hindquarters,
the water depth, and the treatment of costume and foliage.
Also, inscribed on the saddle in the Booth engraving
is « W. Ranney - 50. » The date is omitted
in the American Art-Union painting.
In addition, Booth's commission derived from the Western
Art-Union, not the American Art-Union,
and most certainly he would have used their version
for his source. A number of copies of this popular subject,
doubtless painted after the engraving,
have appeared in recent years. Apparently still another
version by Ranney was included in the Ranney Fund
sale of 1858 (*Fund Catalogue*, No. 178).

Commenting on the American Art-Union version,
the *Herald* critic stated on September 8, 1850,
that this was « a picture of strong character and well
managed. The intense eagerness of the horseman
is admirably conveyed. » In a review
of the nineteenth-century painting exhibition
held at the Harry Shaw Newman Gallery in 1947,
the *Art News*, October, 1947, maintained:

> William Ranney's THE LAST SHOT steals the show.
> Famous when first painted in 1850,
> it became known to thousands through
> Currier & Ives engravings.
> The cornered hunter plunging through
> the swamps on his frantic steed in flight from a
> nameless and invisible enemy might well
> symbolize the last stand of Romanticism
> against the urban civilization of that
> tragic era.

Harold McCracken, in his introduction to the Eberstadt
Catalogue, felt that this was one of the best known
pictures of the Old West and suggested that the subject
was the noted trapper, Joe Meek.

43

THE LAZY FISHERMAN

present owner: Location unknown
verified date: c. 1850
size: c. 27×34
exhibitions:

American Art-Union, N. Y., 1850, No. 320

collections:

American Art-Union, N. Y.; Mr. Cyrus Cole,
Springfield, Mass.

references:

69, xxxi; 172, xv, Dec. 16; 162, vii, Dec. 17, 21;
159, ii, Dec. 18, 21;
172, xv, Dec. 21; 69, xxxvi, p. 174; 10, Vol. II, p. 295

comment:

The Art-Union *Bulletin* for August, 1850, stated:
« Mr. Ranney has lately completed a work called
the 'Lazy Fisherman,' which shows a close study
of Nature.... » The December 31, 1850,
issue of the *Bulletin* described the painting as

> 'an elderly gentleman' dosing [sic]
> beside a 'murmuring stream', with a
> book in his hand, and a rod lying on
> the ground. Near him is his dog,
> also taking a nap.

44

HALT ON THE PRAIRIE

(*On the Plains*)
present owner: Mr. C. R. Smith,
New York
verified date: 1850
medium, support: oil on canvas
size: 36×54
signed and dated, l. c.: « W. Ranney 50. »
exhibitions:

American Art-Union, N. Y., 1850, No. 121;
Denver Art Museum, Denver, Col.,
« Building the West, » Oct., 1955, No. 71

collections:

American Art-Union, N. Y.; Mrs. E. D. Knower, N. Y.;
Randall Collection, Randall's Island, N. Y.;
James Graham & Sons, N. Y.

references:

69, xxvii, p. 15; 110, vii; 172, x, xiv, xv, Dec. 16;
162, vii, Dec. 17, 21; 159, ii, Dec. 18, 21;
172, xv, Dec. 21; 69, xxxvi,
p. 169; 181; 10, Vol. II, p. 295; 93, p. 30; 78, vii

comment:

The *New York Tribune* critic, in a review
of the American Art-Union paintings on exhibition
prior to the December distribution, expressed
the following opinion (November 27, 1850):

> Ranney's pictures are all weak in color.
> However, they tell their story with spirit
> and success. His later works bear the mark
> of industrious study, and all of them are
> favorites with the public... « Halt on the
> Prairie, » is especially admired, not without
> reason....

The *Herald* article, December 21, 1850, listed
« Mrs. E. D. Noah, N. Y., » as the recipient of the
painting at the Art-Union drawing, which
was probably incorrect. A SKETCH FOR PICTURE,
HALT ON THE PRAIRIE was sold
to « Wood » for eight dollars at the Ranney Fund sale,
1858 (*Fund Catalogue*, No. 93).

45

ON THE WING

(*Wild Duck Shooting – On the Wing*; *Duck Shooting*)
present owner: Newhouse Galleries,
New York
verified date: 1850
medium, support: oil on canvas
size: 30×45
signed and dated, l.c.: « W. Ranney / 1850 »

exhibitions:

National Academy of Design, N. Y.,
« Twenty-Fifth Annual Exhibition, » 1850, No. 111;
American Art-Union, N. Y., 1850, No. 224;
U.S. Sanitary Commission, Philadelphia, « Great Central
Fair, » June, 1864, No. 510

collections:

American Art-Union, N. Y.; Mr. John Brodhead;
Mr. Ferdinand J. Drew; Dr. T. A. Read [?];
Abigail P. Drew Read, all of Philadelphia;
Private Western Collection [?]

references:

120, vi, p. 16; 110, viii; 69, xxviii, p. 21;
172, xii; 69, xxix, xxxii, p. 88; 162, vi;
69, xxxiii, facing p. 113, 115; 172, xv, Dec. 16;
162, vii, Dec. 17, 21; 159, ii, Dec. 18, 21;
172, xv, Dec. 21;
69, xxxvi, p. 172, xlv, p. 8; 182, i; 70, iii, p. 15;
162, xii, Dec. 18; 43, facing p. 141; 180; 14, p. 291;
137, p. 18; 2, p. 25; 181; 63, p. 181;
27, p. 772; 76; 28, p. 549; 128; 46, pp. 129, 397;
5, p. 285; 17, p. 377; 11, Vol. II, p. 88;
72, ii; 85, i, p. 464; 10, Vol. I, p. 259, Vol. II, p. 295

comment:

A steel engraving (5×7½) was made for the American

Art-Union by Charles Burt, and was published
in the *Bulletin* for October, 1850 (No. 198).
Along with the engraving of BOONE'S FIRST VIEW
OF KENTUCKY, the cut for ON THE WING was purchased
by Mr. Appleton at the 1852 Art-Union auction,
and appeared subsequently in the *Ornaments of Memory*
(1856 & 1857), as well as a colored version.
Currier & Ives adapted the theme in later lithographs.
Apparently several versions of this work were
painted by Ranney (see Nos. 46, 62).
However, No. 45 is the only signed painting known,
and its provenance may be traced back to 1858,
when it was purchased by Mr. Ferdinand J. Drew
of Philadelphia. It was said to have been
in the possession of the Drew family until its acquisition
by the Newhouse Galleries.
In all probability, this was the painting which appeared
first in the National Academy Exhibition during
the spring of 1850 and, as had become the custom,
was procured by the American Art-Union
for its annual distribution held in December.
The *Catalogue* for the National Academy Exhibition
indicated the painting was for sale.
The *Herald* critic felt « ... there is much earnestness
in the figures, » while *The Literary World* of May 4,
1850, had no reservations in its enthusiastic commentary,
calling the painting « ... capital, in its style.
Sportsman and dog are both in the best spirits,
and are transferred to the canvas without losing
anything of their keen relish of the sport. »
A painting entitled DUCK SHOOTING was purchased
at the Ranney Fund sale in 1858 by « Wood »
for twenty-seven dollars (*Fund Catalogue*, No. 118).

46

ON THE WING

(*Wild Duck Shooting – On the wing*)
present owner: J. N. Bartfield Gallery, Inc.
New York City
verified date: c. 1850
medium, support: oil on canvas
size: 30×45
Contemporary Philadelphia framer's label on back
of stretcher: « Julius Scholz / No. 115 (late 47)
S. Eighth Street, Philadelphia, Pa. / Importer of /
English Plain, Roman, Ticken and German Plain
Twilled Canvas / Ticken Canvas Size 30×45 »

collection:

Mr. R. B. Honeyman, Jr., New York

references:

78, viii

comment:

An excellent painting, well within one's expectations
of Ranney painting one of his favorite themes.
The strongly modeled man is especially well done,
and the treatment of the foliage
and other accessories is consistent with Ranney's manner.
Other versions of this theme were recorded
in the *Brooklyn Eagle*, (January 28, 1945)
[Plaza Art Galleries]; *Antiques* (May, 1945,
and November, 1952), *Art Digest*, (May 1, 1945,
and May 1, 1946, with slightly different dimensions)
[Kennedy Galleries]. Other versions, probably
copies after the engraving, are known.

THE PIONEERS

(*Pioneers with covered Wagons; Emigrant Train*)
present owner: Mr. Claude J. Ranney,
Malvern, Pennsylvania
verified date: c. 1850-57
medium, support: oil on canvas
size: 24×36
signed, l. r.: « W. Ranney » [Not a characteristic
signature; doubtless by another hand]
inscribed on stretcher: « Brady »

exhibitions:

American Art Association, Anderson Galleries, N. Y.,
Jan., 1939, No. 51; M. Knoedler and Company, N. Y.,
« The Opening of the West, » 1949;
City Art Museum of St. Louis, St. Louis, Mo.,
« Westward the Way, » Oct. 22-Dec. 6, 1954, No. 144;
Walker Art Center, Minneapolis, Minn.,
« Westward the Way, » Jan. 4-Feb. 28, 1955, No. 144;
Jefferson National Expansion Memorial, St. Louis, Mo.,
1957 [colored reproduction]; William Rockhill Nelson
Gallery and Mary Atkins Museum of Fine Arts,
Kansas City, Mo., « The Last Frontier, »
Oct. 5-Nov. 17, 1957, No. 46

collections:

Mr. James Topham Brady, N. Y.; Mr. Nathaniel Jarvis,
and daughters of J. T. Brady;
Mr. Michael de Sherbenin, N. Y.;
Mortimer Brandt Galleries, N. Y.;
McClees Gallery, Philadelphia; Mr. J. Clifton Buck

references:

68; 109, i; 131, pp. 181, 268; 144, pp. 10, 24; 155

comment:

In a letter to the *New York Herald*,
May 30, 1853, Brigham Young had the following
advice for the overland emigrants:

> ... They should consider before they start
> on this journey, that now, if never before,
> will be taxed, and brought into requisition,
> all their forbearance, courtesy, patience,
> manhood, vigilance, untiring perseverance,
> and charitable feelings. Perhaps there is
> no one thing that will try a man in all
> these virtues equal to a trip with ox-teams
> across the Plains...

Randolph B. Marcy, in *The Prairie Traveler*, 1863,
estimated the average speed of an ox at about
three miles an hour.

According to the artist's grandson and present owner,
the painting was unfinished and in the artist's studio
at the time of his death. It was given or sold at that
time to James Topham Brady, the lawyer,
by the artist's widow, Margaret Ranney.

While the painting was in a later collection,
the signature was added. Portions of the picture,
such as the man holding the rifle,
and the lower sections of the oxen,
appear too suggestive and weak,
lacking the firm modeling characteristic of Ranney
at his best, as exemplified in the excellent portrayal
of the horse on the left.

DUCK SHOOTING

(*The Retrieve; The Retriever*)
present owner: The Corcoran Gallery of Art,
Washington, D. C.
verified date: 1850
medium, support: oil on canvas
size: 30¼×40³/₈
signed and dated, l. c.: « W. Ranney / 1850 »

exhibitions:

National Academy of Design, N. Y.,
« Twenty-Sixth Annual Exhibition, » 1851, No. 365;
Museum of Fine Arts, Boston, « Sport in American Art, »
Oct. 10-Dec. 10, 1944, No. 82;
Denver Art Museum, Denver, Col., « Man at Work, »
Mar. 2-April 30, 1952; Baltimore Museum of Art,
« Shooting And Fishing In Art, » May 20-June 22,
1958, No. 22

collection:

Mr. William W. Corcoran, Washington, D. C.

references:

120, vii, p. 26; 90, i; 92, i; 58, p. 632;
90, ii, iii, iv; 181; 90, v, vi; 63, p. 181;
90, vii, viii; 27, p. 772; 90, ix, x, xi, xii, xiii;
60, 1912, p. 88; 90, xiv; 28, p. 549; 90, xv, xvi, xvii,
xviii, xix; 145, i; 19, p. 294; 90, xx, xxi; 177, iii, p. 9;
11, Vol. II, p. 89; 85, iii; 90, xxii; 38, p. 225;
83; 177, v, i

comment:

Charles Lanman, the artist, compiled the first
catalogue of Mr. Corcoran's collection (1857),
in which he commented in the following manner
on Ranney's painting:

> This is truly an American Picture,
> and the style is one which the Artist
> has attained a high reputation.

According to Mr. Claude J. Ranney, the kneeling
figure was identified as Richard Ranney (1815-1859),
the brother of the artist. The standing figure
may have been a neighbor's groom,
who was sometimes used as a model by Ranney.
The scene of the painting may have been the Hackensack
Meadows, possibly within the view from
the artist's studio.

HALT ON THE PRAIRIE

(*Caravan on the prairies*)
present owner: Mr. and Mrs. John F. Merriam,.
Omaha, Nebraska
verified date: c. 1850
medium, support: oil on canvas
size: 8×14½

exhibitions:

City Art Museum of St. Louis, St. Louis, Mo.,
« Westward the Way, » Oct. 22-Dec. 6, 1954, No. 145;
Walker Art Center, Minneapolis, Minn.,
« Westward the Way, » Jan. 4-Feb. 28, 1955, No. 145;
William Rockhill Nelson Gallery and Mary Atkins
Museum of Fine Arts, Kansas City, Mo.,
« The Last Frontier, » Oct. 5-Nov. 17, 1957, No. 45.

references:

131, pp. 182, 268; 144, p. 10

comment:

A small sketch, perhaps a study
for a larger work, painted with a more fluid
brushwork than found in Ranney's finished
paintings. Possibly this was the SKETCH FOR PICTURE,
HALT ON THE PRAIRIE which was sold to « Wood »
for eight dollars at the Ranney Fund
sale in 1858 (*Fund Catalogue*, No. 93).

50

THE POST RIDER

present owner: Mr. Gerald D. Hamilton,
Bingham, Maine
verified date: c. 1850
medium, support: oil on canvas
size: 14×17
signed, l. l.: « W. Ranney »
exhibitions:

American Art-Union, N. Y., 1850, No. 349;
Ehrich-Newhouse Galleries, N. Y., « Early American
Genre Paintings, » Dec. 19, 1934-Jan. 5, 1935.

collections:

American Art-Union, N. Y.;
Mr. Isaac Stebbins, Chelsea, Mass.;
Fridenberg Gallery, N. Y.;
Savoy Art & Auction Galleries, N. Y. [?]

references:

172, xv, Dec. 16, 21; 162, vii, Dec. 17, 21;
159, ii, Dec. 18, 21;
69, xxxvi, p. 175; 10, Vol. II, p. 295

comment:

Described in the Art-Union *Bulletin*
as « a man on horseback, riding through the snow,
and among bleak and wild hills. »
A picture by Ranney called the EXPRESS RIDER
was purchased for twelve dollars by Nason Collins
at the Ranney Fund sale, 1858
(*Fund Catalogue*, No. 138).

51

THE RETREAT

present owner: M. Knoedler and Company,
New York
verified date: 1850
medium, support: oil on canvas
size: 30½×48½
signed and dated, l. r.: « W. Ranney / 1850 »
initialed on pack horse: « W. R. »
exhibitions:

National Academy of Design, N. Y.,
« Twenty-Sixth Annual Exhibition, » 1851, No. 123;
Knoedler Galleries, N. Y., « The Far West, »
Feb. 7-26, 1949, No. 37; Philbrook Art Center,
Tulsa, Okla., « Masterpieces of the Month, » 1949;
City Art Museum of St. Louis, St. Louis, Mo.,
« Westward the Way, » Oct. 22-Dec. 6, 1954, No. 147;
Walker Art Center, Minneapolis, Minn.,
« Westward the Way, » Jan. 4-Feb. 28, 1955, No. 147

collections:

Mr. John Wolfe; Coleman Galleries, N. Y.;
Dr. Frederick H. Wilke, N. Y.;
Mr. T. Gilbert Brouillette, Falmouth, Mass.;
Mr. Clendenning Ryan, N. Y.

references:

120, vii, p. 17; 172, xviii; 170, i;
11, Vol. II, p. 89; 107, No. 37; 170, ii;
109, i, p. 42; 131, pp. 185, 268

comment:

In a review of the National Academy show found
in the *New-York Tribune*, June 21, 1851,
Ranney's THE RETREAT was described as having

    ... good movement. The spirit of the
    whole and the concentration of the action
    are very admirable. We could have
    wished a more spacious view of the Prairie,
    which by its vastness and magnificent
    monotony of line would have intensified
    the interest by revealing no rocks,
    or trees, or devices of escape.
    But the scene throbs with characteristic life....

In an article in the *Sun*, May 28, 1938,
it was pointed out that, prior to the Coleman sale,
the painting had been privately owned
for eighty-seven years. However, the article may
have gone too far in suggesting
that the scene depicted by Ranney might
be an incident experienced by the artist,
simply because he had painted his initials
in the form of a brand on one of the horses.

52

PORTRAIT OF MARGARET RANNEY, WIFE OF THE ARTIST

present owner: Mr. Claude J. Ranney,
Malvern, Pennsylvania
medium, support: oil on canvas
size: 30×25½.

53

PORTRAIT OF MARGARET RANNEY, WIFE OF THE ARTIST

present owner: Miss Margaret Ranney,
Union City, New Jersey
medium, support: oil on canvas.

54

PORTRAIT OF JAMES RANNEY, SON OF THE ARTIST

present owner: Miss Margaret Ranney,
Malvern, Pennsylvania
medium, support: oil on canvas
size: 17×13³/₄
printed on back of canvas: « S. N. Dodge's /
Artists & Painters Supply Store / 189 Chatham Cor /
of Oliver St. / New York. »

55

PORTRAIT OF EDWIN WHITE

present owner: Mr. Claude J. Ranney,
Malvern, Pennsylvania
verified date: c. 1850's
medium, support: oil on canvas
size: 17¼×14½
initialed, l. r.: « W. R. »

comment:

Edwin White, N. A. (1817-1877), a friend of Ranney,
was an artist who was best known for his historical
paintings, although he also did genre and portraiture.
Groce and Wallace (1957) mention that he lived
in New York during the 1840's, and studied
in Europe between 1850-1858 [sic].
He must have left for Europe later in 1850 for,
in an article discussing the activities of New York artists,
New York Tribune, April 6, 1850, it was stated
that « Mr. White has nearly completed an historical scene,
in which Queen Catherine and Woolsey are introduced. »
Both French, in *Art and Artists in Connecticut*, 1879,
and a note in *The Knickerbocker*, July, 1856,
pointed out that he returned in 1856.
The latter source commented:
« Edwin White has lately returned from Europe,
and opened a studio in the New-York University,
with ample proof of careful studies.... »
Since Ranney died in November, 1857,
this portrait must have been painted either
during the first part of 1850, or earlier,
or between 1856 and 1857. The large painting
sketchily indicated on the easel at the right was probably
intended to convey the idea of a history-type picture.
It has not been identified.

56

MARION CROSSING THE PEDEE

(*General Marion Crossing the Pee Dee River, S. C.*;
Marion and his men; *Marion and his men
crossing the Pedee*;
Marion, with his army, crossing the Pedee;
General Francis Marion crossing the Pee Dee River;
*Marion's Brigade crossing the Pedee River, S. C.
1778 on their way to attack the British Forces
under Tarleton*)
present owner: Location unknown
verified date: 1850
medium, support: oil on canvas [?]
size: c. 50×74½

exhibitions:

American Art-Union, N. Y., 1851, No. 348;
Miner's Art Galleries, N. Y., March, 1876, No. 43

collections:

American Art-Union, N. Y.; Mr. William H. Webb, N. Y.

references:

69, xxxi, xxxii,
xxxiv, pp. 138-39, xxxvi, p. 88;
100, i; 69, xxxvii, xxxviii; 162, viii;
172, xvii; 100, ii; 69, xl, xliii, xliv, xlv, p. 7;
162, ix, Dec. 3; 182, ii; 70, iii, p. 13;
172, xx, Dec. 18; 110, xiii; 180; 14, p. 291;
2, p. 25; 117, p. 16; 181; 76; 60, 1912, p. 89;
78, i; 153; 64, p. 243; 46, p. 308; 17, p. 377; 147;
189; 72, i; 40, p. 522; 72 ,ii; 9, p. 175;
109, ii; 187; 10, Vol. I, pp. 234, 293, 302,
Vol. II, p. 295; 31, pp. 340, 380; 115

comment:

The hopes of the American Revolutionary forces
in the South centered heavily on three leaders,
Generals Daniel Morgan (the victor at Cowpens),
Thomas Sumter, and Francis Marion.
John Frost, in the *Pictorial Life of General Marion*,
1847, mentioned the famous horse Marion rode,
which was named Ball, after his former master,
the Loyalist Captain Ball, who fell at the battle
of Black Mingo. One of Marion's major adversaries was
Col. Banastre Tarleton, who called him
the « Swamp Fox » because of Marion's
uncanny ability to maneuver through
the Southern marshes.
The incident portrayed by Ranney has not been
specifically identified, but perhaps occurred
shortly after he was appointed Brigadier General,
in November, 1780, and assumed
command of his troops.

> ... On the second or third day after his
> arrival, General Marion ordered his men to
> mount white cockades, to distinguish
> themselves from the tories, and crossed
> the Pedee, at Port's ferry, to disperse a large
> body of tories, under Major Gainey....
>
> William Dobein James, *A Sketch of
> the Life of Brig. Gen. Francis Marion
> ... 1948 ed.*

Ranney's original painting was last reported
in the collection of Mr. William H. Webb,
the New York shipbuilder, who purchased it for nine
hundred dollars at the auction sale of the American
Art-Union holdings in 1852. Presumably, it was sold
in 1876 at the Webb sale,
for it appeared in that *Catalogue*.
Its later whereabouts have not been determined.
Several copies are known. One was
in the possession of the Douthitt Galleries,
New York, from which the large,
colored reproduction for WESTVACO's 1947
calendar was made. Another, said to have
measured 30×45 inches, was in the collection
of Mr. Preston Davie, destroyed by fire.
A third copy was painted by Edward Arnold
(1824/26-1866), now in the Florence Museum,
Florence, South Carolina, the gift
of Mr. and Mrs. W. E. Groves of New Orleans.
Another copy after Ranney's work, by an unknown
artist, and measuring 31×46 inches,
is in the Argosy Gallery, New York.
The American Art-Union selected Ranney's
painting of MARION CROSSING THE PEDEE as one of
a group of five from which steel engravings were
executed comprising a set of engravings called
« The Gallery of American Art. »
This set was distributed to each member of 1851,
along with a large engraving after Richard Caton
Woodville's MEXICAN NEWS.
The print after Ranney's work was engraved
by Charles Burt and printed by J. Dalton
(7½×10, No. 199). Currier and Ives
also published a print of this subject.
Contemporary opinion of Ranney's painting
was generally very high;
most seemed to feel it was one of his
best efforts.
The *Bulletin* for November, 1850, kept its readers
informed of the progress of the painting,
saying it would soon be completed.

In December, 1850, the *Bulletin* devoted
a large section to the paintings which had been
selected for the « Gallery of American Art » engravings.

> Marion and his Men. This is an excellent
> picture, by W. Ranney, but recently finished,
> and which has never been publicly exhibited.

Similar favorable comments were made in the various
issues of the *Bulletin* during the following year,
and the trend was followed by other publications.
After the Art-Union sale in 1852,
the *New York Herald*, December 18, 1852,
reported: « MARION CROSSING THE PEDEE,
which cost the Art Union about $450 [actually $745],
was knocked down, amidst great applause,
to W. H. Webb for $900. »
A parallel with Emanuel Leutze's (1816-1868)
WASHINGTON CROSSING THE DELAWARE of the same
period seems obvious. It is of some interest to note
that Leutze's painting was also acquired
by William H. Webb, and that both his
and Ranney's were included in the Webb sale of 1876.

57

THE TRAPPERS

present owner: M. Knoedler and Company,
New York
verified date: 1851
medium, support: oil on canvas
size: 23×36
signed and dated, l.c.: « Wm. Ranney / 1851 »
exhibitions:
City Art Museum of St. Louis, St. Louis, Mo.,
« Westward the Way, » Oct. 22-Dec. 6, 1954, No. 146;
Walker Art Center, Minneapolis, Minn.,
« Westward the Way, » Jan. 4-Feb. 28, 1955, No. 146;
Denver Art Museum, Denver, Col.,
« Building The West, » Oct., 1955, No. 72
collection:
Collins Gallery, N.Y.
references:
131, pp. 183, 268; 93, pp. 9, 30.

58

ELK HUNTING

(*Elk Hunters – Buckskin Guide and Indian;
Deer Hunting in the Adirondacks* [?])
present owner: Thomas Gilcrease Institute
of American History and Art,
Tulsa, Oklahoma
verified date: 1851
medium, support: oil on canvas
size: 14½×24½
signed and dated, l.l.: « Wm. Ranney 1851 »
exhibitions:
Wanamaker's Sale, N.Y., March, 1936, No. 30
collections:
Mr. Rodman Wanamaker, N.Y.;
with American Artist Association, N.Y.;
Mr. T. Gilbert Brouillette, Falmouth, Mass.;
Mr. Claude J. Ranney, Malvern, Pa.
reference:
67.

59

THE OLD OAKEN BUCKET

(*The sportsman's halt at the well*)
present owner: M. Knoedler and Company,
New York
verified date: 1851
medium, support: oil on canvas
size: 14×19¼
signed and dated, l.l.: « W. Ranney / 51 »
collections:
Mr. Marshall O. Roberts, N.Y.;
Mrs. Marshall O. Roberts, N.Y.;
John Levy Galleries, N.Y.
references:
92, iv; 58, pp. 431, 626; 54, Vol. II, p. 16;
95, p. 69; 97; 52, p. 268; 17, p. 377
comment:
A popular, sentimental genre subject in the arts.
Whether Ranney's production has any connection
with Samuel Woodworth's (1784-1842)
poem of the same title is uncertain,
but another painting entitled
THE OLD OAKEN BUCKET, by J. T. Peele,
was included in the Western Art-Union distribution
in January, 1851, No. 464. Jerome B. Thompson
(1814-1886) painted his interpretation of this theme
in 1860, possibly deriving some inspiration
from his figures at the well from Ranney's earlier work.
(See *The Kennedy Quarterly*, Dec., 1960,
p. 19, No. 17 illus.)
The dimensions given for Ranney's painting
in the Roberts sale *Catalogue*
of 1897 were 19×23½.

60

THE SCOUTING PARTY

(*Scouts*)
present owner: M. Knoedler and Company,
New York
verified date: 1851
medium, support: oil on canvas
size: 22×36
signed and dated, l.c.: « W. Ranney / 51 »
exhibitions:
National Academy of Design, N.Y.,
« Twenty-Sixth Annual Exhibition, » 1851, No. 201;
American Art-Union, N.Y., 1851, No. 252,
and 1852, No. 228
collections:
American Art-Union, N.Y.; J. Yoeman;
Mr. Fred N. Maloof, Washington, D.C.
references:
120, vii, p. 20; 69, xli, xlii; 172, xix;
162, ix, Dec. 10; 69, xlv, pp. 5, 8;
70, iii, pp. 9, 15; 172, xx, Dec. 17; 162, xii;
11, Vol. II, p. 89; 10, Vol. I, pp. 261,
302, Vol. II, p. 295
comment:
The Art-Union publications for 1851-1852
described the scene as « a party of trappers
with their horses on a high bluff watching

the movements of Indians who are betrayed by fires
in the prairies below. »
A woodcut, engraved by Richardson
from a drawing by William R. Miller
after Ranney's painting, was reproduced
in the September 1, 1851, issue
of the Art-Union *Bulletin* (No. 200).

61

THE SCOUTING PARTY

(*The Scouts*)
present owner: Mr. Claude J. Ranney,
Malvern, Pennsylvania
verified date: c. 1851
medium, support: oil on canvas
size: 30×40
signed and dated, l. l.: « Wm. Ranny [sic?] 18[51?] »
exhibitions:
Newhouse Galleries, N. Y.,
« The Second Annual Exhibition of American Genre
Paintings Depicting the Pioneer Period, »
Dec. 22, 1933-Jan. 31, 1934, No. 48;
Metropolitan Museum of Art, N. Y.,
« Life in America, » April 24-Oct. 29, 1939,
No. 136; Knoedler Galleries, N. Y., « The Far West, »
Feb. 7-26, 1949, No. 39; City Art Museum of St. Louis,
St. Louis, Mo., « Westward the Way, »
Oct. 22-Dec. 6, 1954, No. 148;
Walker Art Center, Minneapolis, Minn.,
« Westward the Way, » Jan. 4-Feb. 28, 1955, No. 148;
Jefferson National Expansion Memorial,
St. Louis, Mo., 1957 [colored reproduction]
collection:
Kennedy Galleries, N. Y.

references:

146, ii; 122; 79, i; 171, iv;
116, i, ii; 79, ii; 188; 47, p. 45;
40, p. 522; 107, No. 39; 131, pp. 185, 268
comment:
A painting entitled SCOUTS ON THE PRAIRIE
was sold to « Wood » for sixty-two dollars
and fifty cents at the Ranney Fund sale, 1858
(*Fund Catalogue*, No. 159).

62

THE RETRIEVE

present owner: Location unknown
verified date: c. 1852
exhibitions:
National Academy of Design, N. Y.,
« Twenty-Seventh Annual Exhibition, » 1852, No. 340
collection:
D. L. Suydam
references:
120, viii, p. 25; 162, xi; 11, Vol. II, p. 89
comment:
Possibly a copy or another version
of DUCK SHOOTING (THE RETRIEVE)
in the Corcoran Gallery of Art (No. 48).
The *Herald*, April 21, 1852, mentioned that
« the figure of the dog deserves special notice. »

63

DUCK SHOOTING

present owner: Location unknown
collection: With Williams, Stevens & Williams, N. Y.,
1852
references:
110, xii
comment:
It is not known whether this may have
been the painting exhibited at the National Academy
earlier in 1852 (No. 62) and purchased
at that time by D. L. Suydam. At the Williams,
Stevens & Williams sale, DUCK SHOOTING
sold for forty-two dollars and fifty cents.

64

THE SLEIGH RIDE

(*Boys let out of school*; *Returning from school*)
present owner: Suffolk County Historical Society,
Riverhead, Long Island, New York
verified date: 1852
medium, support: oil on canvas
size: 30×40
signed and dated on stone, l. l.: « W. Ranney / 1852 »
exhibitions:
National Academy of Design, N. Y.,
« Twenty-Seventh Annual Exhibition, » 1852, No. 100;
Miner's Art Galleries, N. Y., March, 1876, No. 15
collections:
With Williams, Stevens & Williams, N. Y., 1852;
Mr. William H. Webb, N. Y.;
Mr. Jordan L. Mott, N. Y. [?]; Mrs. McLean, N. Y.;
Dr. Edward Perkins, Brooklyn; Miss Clara Perkins,
Riverhead, L. I. Mrs. George Perkins, Riverhead, L. I.
references:
120, viii, p. 15; 162, xi; 110, xii; 14, p. 291;
65, No. 29; 117, p. 9; 181; 63, p. 181; 76;
153; 11, Vol. II, p. 89
comment:
The *Herald*, April 21, 1852, called this
« ... an animated and well painted piece.
The countenances of the occupants of the sleigh,
especially the old driver, is harmoniously natural. »

65

LANDSCAPE WITH SCHOOL HOUSE
present owner: Mr. Claude J. Ranney,
Malvern, Pennsylvania
medium, support: oil on canvas, unmounted
size: 10½×14⁵/₈
comment:
A study, possibly related to No. 64.

66

SQUIRE BOONE CROSSING THE MOUNTAINS
WITH STORES FOR HIS BROTHER
DANIEL, ENCAMPED IN THE WILDS OF KENTUCKY

present owner: Miss Amelia Peabody,
Boston, Massachusetts
verified date: 1852

medium, support: oil on canvas
size: 36 × 32½
signed and dated, l. r.: « W. Ranney / '52 »

exhibitions:

National Academy of Design, N. Y.,
« Twenty-Eighth Annual Exhibition, » 1853, No. 80;
Vose Galleries, Boston, « A Loan Exhibition Honoring
Robert Churchill Vose, » March 7-25, 1961, No. 27

collections:

Edward D. Nelson; Vose Galleries of Boston

references:

120, ix, p. 14; 162, xiii, May 23;
11, Vol. II, p. 89; 140, iii

comment:

The incident portrayed by Ranney in this painting
occurred after the scene described
in his BOONE'S FIRST VIEW OF KENTUCKY (Nos. 38, 39).
In the words of Boone, as given by Filson
and quoted in William H. Bogart's
Daniel Boone, and the Hunters of Kentucky, 1854:

> At this place we encamped, and made a shelter
> to defend us from the inclement season,
> and began to hunt, and reconnoiter the country.
> We found everywhere abundance of wild beasts
> of all sorts, through this vast forest.
> The buffalo were more frequent than I have ever
> seen cattle in the settlements, browsing
> on the leaves of the cane, or cropping
> the herbage on those extensive plains, fearless,
> because ignorant of the violence of man.... About
> this time my brother, Squire Boone,
> with another adventurer... was wandering through
> the forest and accidentally found
> our camp.... Soon after this my companion
> in captivity, John Stewart, was killed
> by the savages, and the man that came
> with my brother returned home by himself.
> We were then in a dangerous, helpless situation,
> exposed daily to perils and death amongst
> the savages and wild beasts – not a white man
> in the country but ourselves.
> Thus situated, many hundred miles from
> our families, in the howling wilderness,
> I believe few would have equally enjoyed
> the happiness we experienced.
> We continued not in a state of indolence,
> but hunted every day, and prepared a little
> cottage to defend us from the winter storms.
> We remained there undisturbed during the winter.
> On the first of May, 1770, my brother
> returned home to the settlement by himself,
> for a new recruit of horses and ammunition,
> leaving me by myself, without bread, salt
> or sugar, without company of my fellow-creatures,
> or even a horse or dog.

Some confusion has arisen in recent times
regarding this painting and two others (Nos. 71, 72),
all of which have been identified at various
times with the Squire Boone exhibited
at the National Academy of Design in 1853.
That the Boston painting, No. 66,
is the correct one is proved conclusively
by a description in a review of the Academy
show found in the *New York Herald*, May 23, 1853.

> No. 80. Squire Boon [sic; Boone's name
> was frequently spelled without the « e »]

crossing the mountains with stores for
his brother Daniel, encamped in the wilds
of Kentucky. Painted by W. Ranney, associate.
Possessor, Edward D. Nelson.
Boon is represented on horseback and is
evidently listening around if any Indians are near.
The bold, careless hunter, is well depicted,
but perhaps the figure is too youthful.

It may be noted, also, that Squire Boone's journey
took place during the summer season.
According to the literary sources, he left May 1,
1770, and returned July 27.

67

WINTER IN NEW JERSEY

present owner: Location unknown
verified date: c. 1852

exhibitions:

American Art-Union, N. Y., 1853, No. 170

references:

70, iv.

68

ADVICE ON THE PRAIRIE

(*The old scout's tale*; *The frontiersman*)
present owner: Mr. Claude J. Ranney,
Malvern, Pennsylvania
verified date: 1853
medium, support: oil on canvas
size: 40 × 54
signed and dated, l. c.: « W. Ranney / '53 »

collection:

Mr. Paul H. Bilhuber, N. Y.

comment:

Members of the Ranney family have expressed
the opinion that the figures on the right side
of the group were friends of the artist.
It has also been suggested that the central figure
may be the scout, Jim Bridger, sometimes called
the « Daniel Boone of the Rocky Mountains. »

69

ADVICE ON THE PRAIRIE

(*The old scout's tale*; *The frontiersman*)
present owner: Thomas Gilcrease Institute
of American History and Art,
Tulsa, Oklahoma
medium, support: oil on canvas
size: 14 × 20
initialed, l. c.: « Wm. R. »

exhibitions:

Robert Fridenberg, N. Y.; Frederick Frazier
Gallery, N. Y., « Exhibition of American Genre... »
April 2-May 20, 1938, No. 13;
John Levy Galleries, N. Y., « America in 19th Century, »
May 16-June 9, 1944, No. 22

reference:

102

comment:

A study for No. 68.

DUCK SHOOTER'S PONY

present owner: Mr. George Bernard Wagstaff,
New York
verified date: 1853
signed and dated, l. c.: « W. Ranney / 53 »

exhibitions:

National Academy of Design, N. Y.,
« Twenty-Eighth Annual Exhibition, » 1853, No. 40;
Metropolitan Museum of Art, N. Y.,
« Sporting Prints and Paintings, » 1937

collection:

Mr. Henry C. Coit

references:

120, ix, p. 12; 162, xiii, May 8; 11, Vol. II, p. 89

comment:

Indicative of one type of « criticism »
expressed during this period was that advanced
in the *Herald* review of the Academy exhibition,
May 8, 1853, in which Ranney's painting was
considered to be:

> ... of considerable merit – it shows the hand
> of a draftsman. The old pony,
> with a large bunch of canvasback ducks,
> or red heads, on his back, stands patiently,
> while the old man, his two boys and dogs
> are engrossed with the approach of a flight
> of ducks – the old man has seized
> his gun and all eyes are fixed on the nearing
> of the fowl. In our judgment,
> we should say the artist has made the weather
> appear too warm: the scene is evidently intended
> for the fall, and gunners seldom find ducks
> until much colder weather.
> We should also say, from the small size of the fowling
> piece in the hands of the old gunner,
> that the ducks must have been very accommodating,
> if we may judge from the huge quantity killed.
> The artist has been very happy in giving
> a life-like interest to the whole scene;
> the dogs, in particular, are very natural,
> with their eyes fixed on the flying ducks,
> awaiting only the discharge of the gun to fetch
> the game. It is a very interesting picture – only
> a little too warm.

71

A TRAPPER CROSSING THE MOUNTAINS

(*Squire Boone crossing the mountains into Kentucky*)
present owner: The J. B. Speed Art Museum,
Louisville, Kentucky
verified date: 1853
medium, support: oil on canvas
size: 38 × 33
signed and dated, l. r.: « W. Ranney / 1853 »

references:

59a; 135, i, ii [all entries as SQUIRE
BOONE CROSSING THE MOUNTAINS INTO KENTUCKY]

comment:

See No. 66.

72

A TRAPPER CROSSING THE MOUNTAINS

present owner: Mr. and Mrs. M. D. Johnston,
Los Angeles, California
verified date: c. 1853
medium, support: oil on canvas
size: 30 × 25

exhibitions:

Philbrook Art Center, Tulsa, Okla., 1954;
Wichita Art Association Galleries, Wichita, Kan., 1954

collections:

Private Art Collection, Boston;
Mr. G. Harry Adalian, Boston;
Mrs. G. Harry Adalian, Newton, Mass.;
Mr. T. Gilbert Brouillette, Falmouth, Mass.

comment:

This may have been the painting entitled
A TRAPPER CROSSING THE MOUNTAINS
which was sold to « Walker »
for seventeen dollars at the Ranney Fund
sale in 1858 (*Fund Catalogue*, No. 38).

73

STUDY FOR A LARGE PICTURE

present owner: Location unknown
verified date: c. 1853
exhibitions:
National Academy of Design, N. Y.,
« Twenty-Eighth Annual Exhibition, » 1853, No. 348
collection:
Mr. John B. Moreau
references:
120, ix, p. 25; 11, Vol. II, p. 89.

74

THE SALE OF MANHATTAN BY THE INDIANS

(*Purchase of Manhattan Island from the Indians
by the Dutch, in 1626*)
present owner: Rutgers University,
New Brunswick, New Jersey
verified date: c. 1853
medium, support: oil on canvas
size: 48 × 68
signed, l. c.: « W. Ranney »

exhibitions:
National Academy of Design, N. Y.,
« Twenty-Eighth Annual Exhibition, » 1853, No. 71
collection:
Dr. James Anderson, N. Y.
references:
120, ix, p. 14; 110, xiv; 162, xiii, May 23;
92, vii; 58, p. 431; 62, Vol. I, pp. 152, 156, n. 1;
97; 52, p, 240; 17, p. 377; 11, Vol. II, p. 89.
The painting was described in the National Academy
of Design *Catalogue* as representing

> ... the purchase by the Dutch West India Company,
> of the Island of Manhattan, from the native Indians,
> in the summer of 1626. The principal figure
> is Peter Minuit, the Director General
> of the New Netherlands.
> Behind him is Isaac De Rasieres,

the Provincial Secretary. On Minuit's right,
is Sebastian Jansen Kiol, « Krank-besoeckee, »
whose duty it was to visit the sick
and read the Scriptures and Creeds
to the people on Sunday.

The picture was well received by Ranney's
contemporaries.

Ranney was obviously indebted to Benjamin
West's PENN'S TREATY WITH THE INDIANS
for the general conception and design.
The painting was discovered and identified
as a Ranney in 1923 by Mr. Alexander Stuart Graham,
then Assistant in the Rutgers College Library.
How or when it came to Rutgers has not been
ascertained. According to Wilson's *The Memorial
History of the City of New-York*, 1892,
the work was « ... painted by order of the late
Dr. James Anderson, an Elder for several years
of the Reformed Dutch (Collegiate)
Church of New-York. » The *Catalogue*
for the National Academy exhibition of 1853 recorded
the name of Dr. Anderson as the owner.
Apparently another version, possibly a study,
was included in the Ranney Fund sale of 1858,
where it was bought by « Pepoon » for twenty-six
dollars (*Fund Catalogue*, No. 50).

75

BACKWOODSMEN

present owner: Location unknown
verified date: c. 1853

exhibitions:
American Art-Union, N. Y., 1853, No. 73 [?].

76

COWBOYS – THE BANDITTI
OF '76 FIGHTING OVER THEIR SPOILS
(*Cowboys fighting over their plunder*)
present owner: Location unknown
verified date: c. 1853

exhibitions:
National Academy of Design, N. Y.,
« Twenty-Eighth Annual Exhibition, » 1853, No. 420

collection:
Mr. Thomas W. Phelps

references:
120, ix, p. 28; 180; 14, p. 291;
11, Vol. II, p. 89

comment:
A STUDY FOR LARGE PICTURE OF COW BOYS
QUARRELLING OVER THEIR PLUNDER by Ranney
was sold at the 1858 Ranney Fund sale to « Menzies »
for twenty-two dollars (*Fund Catalogue*, No. 28).

77

THE PACK MULE

present owner: Location unknown

exhibitions:
Williams, Stevens & Williams,
National Academy of Design, N. Y.,
« Second Annual Sale of Paintings, » Nov., 1853

collection:
Williams, Stevens & Williams, N. Y.

references:
162, xvi, Nov. 11

comment:
The *Herald* article stated that this was
« ... a clever picture; coloring very good.
Sold at $95. He should have finished the background. »

78

WINTER SCENE

present owner: Location unknown
collection:
With Henry Leeds and Company, N. Y., 1854

references:
172, xxiv

comment:
The painting was sold for sixty dollars
at the Leeds sale, October 31-November 1, 1854.

79

THE FOWLER'S RETURN

present owner: Location unknown
verified date: c. 1854

exhibitions:
National Academy of Design, N. Y.,
« Twenty-Ninth Annual Exhibition, » 1854, No. 229

references:
120, x, p. 21; 11, Vol. II, p. 89.

80

VIRGINIA WEDDING

present owner: Maryland Historical Society,
Baltimore, Maryland
verified date: 1854
medium, support: oil on canvas
size: 53×81
signed and dated, l. r.: « Wm Ranney 1854 »

exhibitions:
Maryland Historical Society, Baltimore, Md.,
« Sixth Annual Exhibition, » 1858, No. 49;
Charity Art Exchange Exhibition, Baltimore, Md.,
1874, No. 239; Virginia Museum of Fine Arts,
Richmond, Va., « An Exhibition of Nineteenth Century
Virginia Genre, » Jan. 17-Feb. 13, 1946, No. 50

collections:
Dr. Thomas Edmondson; Mr. Samuel Hough;
Mrs. S. J. Hough; The Misses May, Ethel
and Ann E. Hough, all of Baltimore

references:
113, i; 181; 113, ii, iii, iv; 139; 175

comment:
An unidentified clipping from the volume,
The Ranney Collection, in the New York Historical
Society stated:

His « Virginia Wedding » exhibits his powers
to advantage. What a pleasant cavalcade
is that of the youths each with a partner
pillioned behind. The horses enter into

the spirit of the scene, and seem to enjoy
their double burdens as much as the bridegroom
his duplicated responsibilities.

A STUDY OF PICTURE, VIRGINIA WEDDING was sold
to « Menzies » for thirty dollars at the Ranney Fund
sale, 1858 (*Fund Catalogue*, No. 174).

81

WASHINGTON AND GIST CROSSING THE ALLEGHENY RIVER

(*Washington and Gist crossing the Allegheny
River on a raft*)
present owner: The Richard King Mellon Foundation,
Pittsburgh, Pennsylvania
verified date: 1854
medium, support: oil on canvas
size: 39×55
signed and dated, l. l.: « Wm. Ranney / 1854 »
exhibitions:
National Academy of Design, N. Y.,
« Thirtieth Annual Exhibition, » 1855, No. 95;
Robert C. Vose Galleries, Boston, « American
Landscape and Figure Painting, » Summer, 1948, No. 36
collections:
S. N. Dodge, N. Y.; Mr. M. Holt, N. Y.;
Louisa B. Holt, Summit, N. J.;
John Levy Galleries, N. Y.;
McCaughen & Burr, St. Louis, Mo.
references:
120, xi, p. 20; 171, ii, Dec. 20; 85, i, p. 462;
11, Vol. II, p. 89; 140, i, ii, No. 36; 123.
comment:
Ranney's picture, painted a century after
the event occurred, depicts an incident
in the early career of Major George Washington.
English claims in the Ohio Valley were being
threatened by the French. In 1753, Governor Dinwiddie
of Virginia determined to send a messenger
with an official warning to the French commander.
The courier would have to make his way through miles
of uninhabited wilderness during the winter season,
and return immediately with the French reply.
In addition, he was to gather any additional information
he could obtain regarding the strength of the
enemy forces. The youthful and ambitious Washington
volunteered for the job.
On November 15, 1753,
the small party of seven men, horses and baggage
departed. Washington's guide was Christopher Gist,
an intrepid Marylander who had distinguished
himself in the service of the Ohio Company
as an explorer, trader and Indian diplomatist.
The party reached Fort Le Boeuf nearly
one month later and Washington carried out his mission.
On the return trip, Gist and Washington were
confronted with the prospect of crossing the swollen
and ice-filled Allegheny River.
They constructed a raft and managed to negotiate
part of the distance, but the combination of ice
and current forced them to abandon their makeshift
craft in midstream, where they were able to make
their way to a small island. In the words of Gist:

> Saturday 29. – We set out early,
> got to Alleghany, made a raft, and with

much difficulty got over to an island,
a little above Shannopin's town [Pittsburgh].
The Major having fallen in from off the raft,
and my fingers frostbitten, and the sun down,
and very cold, we contented ourselves to encamp
upon that island. It was deep water between
us and the shore; but the cold did us
some service, for in the morning it was frozen
hard enough for us to pass over on the ice...

> William M. Darlington, *Christopher
> Gist's Journals*, 1893.

William Ranney undoubtedly knew of the painting
of this subject by Daniel Huntington,
which was the source of the engraving by Richard
W. Dodson that appeared in *The Gift for 1845* album.
The same firm that printed the engraving,
J. M. Butler, provided another plate
with slight modifications which was printed
in *Graham's Magazine* for August, 1855.
The various versions were probably known
to William Sidney Mount when he painted
his study of this theme in 1863.
(See Cowdrey and Williams, *William Sidney Mount...*,
1944, p. 29, No. 123, Fig. 73).
A STUDY FOR PICTURE, WASHINGTON CROSSING
THE SUSQUEHANNAH was sold to « Wood »
at the Ranney Fund sale, 1858,
for seventeen dollars (*Fund Catalogue*, No. 89).
See No. 24 for another rendition of Washington's 1753
mission by Ranney.

82

EVENING ON THE MEADOWS

present owner: Location unknown
verified date: c. 1855
exhibitions:
National Academy of Design, N. Y.,
« Thirtieth Annual Exhibition, » 1855, No. 101
collection:
S. N. Dodge, N. Y.
references:
120, xi, p. 20; 162, xx; 11, Vol. II, p. 89.
comment:
The *Herald* article on the Academy exhibition stated
that this was « ... a good picture, subdued in tone
and delicate in finish – the cows are especially
well drawn. The only fault we notice is the sky...
there is too much blue. »

83

GOING TO MILL

present owner: Location unknown
verified date: c. 1856
exhibitions:
National Academy of Design, N. Y.,
« Thirty-First Annual Exhibition, » 1856, No. 22
collection:
Mr. Joseph Moreau
references:
120, xii, p. 14; 11, Vol. II, p. 89.

84

THE SKATERS

(*Skater-boys*)
present owner: Location unknown
verified date: c. 1856

exhibitions:
National Academy of Design, N. Y.,
« Thirty-First Annual Exhibition, » 1856, No. 104

references:
120, xii, p. 17; 92, iii; 11, Vol. II, p. 89

comment:
A rather negative opinion was expressed about
this painting in the review of the Academy exhibition
found in *The Crayon*.

> ... We must give Mr. White's picture
> [*Virtuoso*] the credit of being more
> sincere and simple than the others of the class,
> which, with the one agreeing point
> of caring particularly for no truth,
> differ widely in power and sincerity,
> from Ranney's Skater-boys, stiffened under
> the impossible sunlight, in No. 104,
> to the most egregious monstrosity we have ever
> seen on the walls of our Academy exhibitions,
> the Fortune-teller of Mr. Hunt....

85

RAIL SHOOTING

present owner: Location unknown
verified date: 1856-59
medium: oil
size: $13^3/_4 \times 19^1/_2$
signed and dated on side of boat, l. c.: « Wm. Ranney
1856 & W. S. M. 59 »

exhibitions:
Harry Shaw Newman Gallery, N. Y.,
April, 1942, No. 19

collections:
J. Ackerman Coles; Old Print Shop, N. Y.

references:
79, iii; 129

comment:
The locale of this painting is said to have been
Hackensack Meadows, where Ranney himself
often hunted. Several of his unfinished paintings,
left in his studio at the time of his early death,
were completed by other artists.
In this case, it was the noted genre painter,
William Sidney Mount (1807-1868),
who was a good friend of William Ranney.

86

HALT ON THE PLAINS

(*On the plains*)
present owner: Mrs. Eleanor Searle Whitney,
Long Island, New York
medium, support: oil on canvas
size: 46×72

exhibitions:
Vose Galleries, Boston, « American Landscape
and Figure Painters, » Summer, 1948;

Acquavella Galleries, N. Y., 1948;
Brooklyn Museum, N. Y., « Westward Ho, »
Feb. 9-April 10, 1949; Grand Central Art Galleries, N. Y.,
« Remington to Today, » April 5-30, 1955, No. 38

collections:
Count Pedro Massa, Nice, France;
Syracuse Art Museum, N. Y.; Vose Galleries,
Boston, Mass.; Mr. T. Gilbert Brouillette,
Falmouth, Mass.; Mr. Cornelius Vanderbilt Whitney, N. Y.

references:
140, i; 99; 163.

87

SELF-PORTRAIT

present owner: Mr. Claude J. Ranney,
Malvern, Pennsylvania
medium: oil
size: $10^3/_4 \times 9^1/_2$ (Oval).

88

THE MEADOWS

present owner: Location unknown
verified date: c. 1857

exhibitions:
National Academy of Design, N. Y.,
« Thirty-Second Annual Exhibition, » 1857, No. 494

references:
120, xiii, p. 33; 11, Vol. II, p. 89.

89

THE TORY ESCORT

present owner: Miss Margaret Ranney,
Union City, New Jersey
verified date: 1857
medium, support: oil on canvas
size: 36×35
signed and dated, l. r.: « Wm. Ranney, 57 »
Title and signature inscribed on reverse of canvas.

collections:
Mr. Alfred Corning Clark, N. Y.;
Mrs. Margaret Ranney, N. J.

comment:
According to the artist's grandson,
Mr. Claude J. Ranney, the figure riding the horse
at center was Charles Cox, a descendant
of the Cox family who were early settlers
of Hudson County, New Jersey. The other figure
is thought to have been named Neville.
The painting was left in the studio
at the time of the artist's death, and was kept
by Margaret Ranney, the artist's wife, who later
sold it to Mr. Alfred Corning Clark of New York.
When he learned that it was the last painting
she had from her husband's work, Mr. Clark insisted
on returning it to her. The painting has
remained in the Ranney family ever since.
However, a TORIES WITH A PRISONER was sold
at the 1858 Ranney Fund sale for seventy-five dollars
to « Pepoon » (*Fund Catalogue*, No. 81).

90

THE TORY ESCORT

present owner: Mr. Claude J. Ranney,
Malvern, Pennsylvania
medium, support: oil on canvas
size: 14×17
dealer's stencil on back of canvas: « S. N. Dodge's /
Artists & Painters Supply Store / 189 Chatham Cor /
of Oliver St., New York »
inscribed on label, attached to reverse: « 278 »
inscribed in crayon, twice, on frame back: « 278 »
collections:
Mr. Marshall O. Roberts, N. Y.;
Mrs. Marshall O. Roberts, N. Y.; Nicholson Gallery, N. Y.
references:
95, p. 79
A study for No. 85. A TORIES WITH A PRISONER,
doubtless a sketch, judging by the sales price
of eight dollars and fifty cents,
was sold to « Wood » at the Ranney Fund
sale of 1858 (*Fund Catalogue*, No. 96).

91

THE SPY OF WAR

present owner: Location unknown
reference:
153
comment:
Possibly the same as No. 89 or No. 90.

92

THE PIPE OF FRIENDSHIP

present owner: The Newark Museum,
Newark, New Jersey
verified date: 1857-59
medium, support: oil on canvas
size: 23×36
signed, l. c.: « W. Ranney 1857 & W. S. M. Feb. 1859. »
Title inscribed on back of canvas.
exhibitions:
The Newark Museum, N. J., « A Museum in Action, »
Oct. 31, 1944-Jan. 31, 1945, No. 51;
Idem., « Early New Jersey Artists, » Mar.7-May 19,
1957, No. 78; *Idem.*, « Of Other Days, »
June 6-Nov. 17, 1957.
collection: J. Ackerman Coles
references:
12, p. 5; 121, i; 40, p. 522; 121, ii,
pp. 12, 32; 154; 121, iii
comment:
Another Ranney painting completed by William S. Mount.
For a very similar work see THE SCOUTING PARTY, No. 61.
A painting entitled THE TRAPPER'S HALT, described
as « very fine, » was sold to « Dr. Bissell »
for three hundred and forty dollars at the Ranney Fund
sale of 1858 (*Fund Catalogue*, No. 170).

93

RECRUITING DURING THE AMERICAN REVOLUTION

present owner: Location unknown
verified date: c. 1857-59

medium, support: oil on canvas
size: 54×82
inscribed, l. l.: « Painted by W. Ranney, finished
by Blauvelt 1859 »
collections:
Stokes Collection; with Anderson Galleries, N. Y.
reference:
75
comment:
Several artists, in addition to Mount,
assisted in completing unfinished paintings by Ranney.
Charles F. Blauvelt (1824-1900), the portrait
and genre artist, was a member of the National
Academy residing in New York until the early 1860's.
Ranney's composition in this work recalls
some of the election paintings by Bingham.
Perhaps this was the painting entitled
ENLISTING DURING THE REVOLUTIONARY WAR which
was sold to « Brady » for one hundred dollars
at the Ranney Fund sale, 1858.
A STUDY FOR LARGE PICTURE – REVOLUTIONARY
ENLISTMENT was sold to « Pepoon » for twenty-six
dollars at the same sale (*Fund Catalogue*, Nos. 75, 63).

94

THE FRESHET

present owner: Location unknown
verified date: c. 1857-58
medium: oil
size: 15×24
signed, l. r.: « W. Ranney / Otto [Sommer?].
comment:
Apparently another painting completed after
the artist's death. The signature of the second artist
is difficult to read in the existing photograph
and will have to await the recovery
of the painting for corroboration.
An artist by the name of Otto Sommer exhibited
a painting entitled LANDSCAPE WITH DEER, No. 37,
at the Metropolitan Fair held in New York, 1864.
Possibly THE FRESHET was the painting
which was sold to Nason Collins
for fourteen dollars at the Ranney Fund sale,
1858 (*Fund Catalogue*, No. 152).

95

KENTUCKY SCOUTS

present owner: Location unknown
medium, support: oil on canvas
size: 14×20
exhibitions:
American Artist Association, Anderson Galleries, N. Y.,
« American Historical Paintings, » Jan., 1938, No. 52
reference:
68
comment:
The 1938 *Catalogue* cited above described
the painting as « two hardy frontiersmen in red shirts,
buckskin attire and moccasins are holding
their guns ready for an encounter as they peer
toward the distance from a height where large
boulders form quick shelter.

Their mounts, chestnut and white respectively,
are close to them and seem to share their anxiety.
Neutral sky.... It has been suggested
that the subjects are Daniel Boone and Harrod,
after whom Harrodsburg, Ky., is named. »

96

FIRST FISH OF THE SEASON

present owner: Location unknown
collections:
Mr. Joseph Harrison; Mrs. Joseph Harrison,
both of Philadelphia
references:
58, p. 630; 54, Vol. III, p. 92.

97

THE MULETEER

present owner: Location unknown
collection:
Mr. Marshall O. Roberts, N. Y.
references:
58, pp. 431, 626; 97; 17, p. 377.

98

THE TRAVELLER

present owner: Location unknown
exhibitions:
U. S. Sanitary Commission, « Great Central Fair, »
Philadelphia, June, 1864, No. 90
collection:
Mr. Marshall O. Roberts, N. Y.
references:
137, p. 7.

99

THE PIONEER

present owner: Location unknown
size: c. 24×29½
collections:
Mr. Marshall O. Roberts; Mrs. Marshall O. Roberts,
both of N. Y.
references:
54, Vol. II, p. 16; 95, p. 16; 172, xxxi, Jan. 20
comment:
In all probability, this painting,
THE TRAVELLER, No. 98, and THE MULETEER, No. 97,
were the same work. Each was listed separately
in the Roberts Collection at various times
in the nineteenth century.
The painting was sold for fifty-five dollars
at the Roberts sale in 1897.

100

HACKENSACK MEADOWS

present owner: Miss Margaret Ranney,
Union City, New Jersey
medium, support: oil on canvas
size: 14×20.

101

REVOLUTIONARY SOLDIER

present owner: Location unknown
medium, support: oil on academy board
size: 7×5½
Signed [?]
exhibitions:
Parke-Bernet Galleries, N. Y.,
March, 1954, No. 421
collections:
Mr. John S. Clark, Jr.; Agnes Clark,
both of Philadelphia and Alcescot House, Alcescot,
Oxfordshire, England
reference:
126, ii
comment:
Described in the 1954 *Catalogue*
as « ... a young man, wearing a white shirt
and buff breeches, loading his gun,
standing on a rocky platform. »

102

BOYS CRABBING

present owner: Location unknown
reference:
181.

103

THE VICTIM

(*Halt on the prairie – The victim* [?])
present owner: Location unknown
collection:
Count Pedro Massa, Nice, France
reference:
181
comment:
Margaret Ranney, the wife of the artist,
in the questionnaire she completed
for *Appletons' Cyclopaedia of American Biography*,
listed among Ranney's paintings HALT ON THE
PRAIRIE – THE VICTIM (Count Pedro Massa, Nice,
France). Whether she meant two paintings
or one is questionable.
She recorded a HALT ON THE PRAIRIE separately
elsewhere in this source.

104

CATTLE PIECE

present owner: Location unknown
exhibitions:
Dusseldorf Gallery, N. Y., Feb., 1866
references:
172, xxviii
comment:
Ranney's CATTLE PIECE sold for sixty-five
dollars at the Dusseldorf Gallery sale, 1866.

105

BARNYARD; WITH CATTLE — WINTER

present owner: Location unknown

exhibitions:

Dusseldorf Gallery, N. Y., Feb., 1866

references:

172, xxviii

comment:

This work was sold for ninety-five dollars
at the Dusseldorf Gallery sale, 1866.

106

BOY ON HORSE FORDING A STREAM

present owner: Location unknown

collection:

Mrs. M. de Sherbenin.

107

THE CATTLE GUARD

present owner: Location unknown

collections:

Miss Sophia C. V. C. Stevens, Princeton, N. J.;
W. B. Norman

references:

181; 184

comment:

Miss Stevens bequeathed « ... all the residue
of my estate, including the proceeds
of the sale of the painting by Ranney,
which now hangs in my parlor, and represents
a cattle scene, and which I desire sold in New York
or Philadelphia... to the Margaret William Hospital,
Shanghai, China. » The painting was said to have
been purchased for twenty-five dollars
at the sale held in 1894, by W. B. Norman.

108

THE ESCAPE

present owner: Location unknown

collection:

Mr. A. E. Douglass, N. Y.

references:

162, xxi

comment:

Whether this painting was the same
as another known to have been in the collection
of Mr. Douglass and sold at this time,
CROSSING THE FERRY — SCENE ON THE PEDEE
(See No. 15), is uncertain.

The Douglass sale was managed by Henry H. Leeds
and Company, on the occasion of the owner leaving
this country for residence abroad.

Their advertisement referred to the painting
as « ... a superb picture. »

109

PORTRAIT OF A GENTLEMAN

present owner: Location unknown

size: 34×27

Signed [?]

collection:

Private Collection, Mass.

exhibitions:

Parke-Bernet Galleries, N. Y., Feb. 6-7, 1948, No. 80

references:

181, Clipping

comment:

The clipping describes the painting
as a « half-length figure of a man with white hair,
dressed in a black suit with black satin waistcoat
and bow stock; seated to half left, resting
the left arm on the back of his chair.
Signed on chair rail. »

110

STUDY OF A LEDGE

present owner: Mr. Claude J. Ranney,
Malvern, Pennsylvania

medium, support: oil on paper

size: $9 \times 11^3/_8$.

111

LANDSCAPE WITH PINE TREE

present owner: Mr. Claude J. Ranney,
Malvern, Pennsylvania

medium, support: oil on paper

size: $9 \times 11^3/_8$.

112

RIVER WITH BORDER OF TREES

present owner: Mr. Claude J. Ranney,
Malvern, Pennsylvania.

113

LANDSCAPE WITH RAIL FENCES

present owner: Mr. Claude J. Ranney,
Malvern, Pennsylvania

medium, support: oil on paper

size: $9^3/_8 \times 14^1/_2$.

114

STUDY OF A HORSE'S HOOF

present owner: Mr. Claude J. Ranney,
Malvern, Pennsylvania

medium, support: oil on paper

size: $9^1/_2 \times 7^3/_8$.

Note: An unidentified painting, said to be
by William Ranney, was seen recently
in a California private collection.
Unfortunately, it has not been possible
to verify this report at the time
this catalogue went to press.

PART II
WATERCOLORS DRAWINGS

115

STUDY FOR « BOONE'S VIEW OF KENTUCKY, 1769 »

present owner: The J. B. Speed Art Museum,
Louisville, Kentucky
medium: pencil on pink paper
size: c. 9×12, plus margins
inscribed in ink on margin, l. r.: « First thoughts
of "Boones view of Kentucky" / by Ranney. »
[Possibly by the artist.]
inscribed in pencil on margin, l. l.: « On the 7th day
of June 1769 Daniel Boone, / in company
with John Stewart, John Finley [sic Finlay], /
Joseph Holden, James Holden [?], James Mooney
[sic Monay] / and William Cool,
found himself on Red / River and from the top
of an eminence saw / with pleasure the
beautiful level of Kentucky » / so wrote John Filson
in 1785. / Boone and his companions discovering
Kentucky by William T. Ranney A.N.A. 1813-1857. »
reference:
135, iii
comment:
Six full-length figures of men in frontier dress,
carrying guns, and with a dog in the foreground,
are arranged on a plateau, with a suggestion
of rocks and trees in the background.
Obviously a study for the large paintings of the
same subject, Nos. 38 and 39.

116

THE SPORTSMAN AND HIS DOG

present owner: Location unknown
medium: tinted drawing
size: c. 5×6
exhibitions:
National Academy of Design, N. Y.,
Johnston Sale, Nov. 29-Dec. 19, 1876, No. 316
collection:
Mr. John Taylor Johnston, N. Y.
references:
86; 172, xxx
comment:
The drawing was sold for twenty-one dollars
at the Johnston sale.

117

FARMHOUSE WITH DOVECOTE

present owner: Museum of Fine Arts, Boston,
M. and M. Karolik Collection
medium: pencil
size: $3^3/_8 \times 4^5/_8$
initialed, l. r.: « R ».

118

TWO DISTURBED ONLOOKERS

present owner: Museum of Fine Arts, Boston,
M. and M. Karolik Collection
medium: pen and ink [over pencil?]
size: $7^1/_2 \times 5^3/_8$.

119

MAN WITH DOGS ON LEASH

present owner: Museum of Fine Arts, Boston,
M. and M. Karolik Collection
medium: pen and ink
size: $4^3/_4 \times 5^1/_2$ (within margins).

120

CHILDREN UNDER UMBRELLA

present owner: Museum of Fine Arts, Boston,
M. and M. Karolik Collection
medium: pencil
size: $5^1/_8 \times 4$.

121

SLEEPING DOG

present owner: Museum of Fine Arts, Boston,
M. and M. Karolik Collection
medium: pencil
size: $3^1/_8 \times 5$
comment:
Nos. 120 and 121 are pasted on page 38
in the « Falconer Album. » The Album was formed
by the artist, John Mackie Falconer (1820-1903)
of New York. It contains drawings by his contemporaries,
some of whom were his friends.
Mr. Claude J. Ranney thought the SLEEPING DOG
might be William Ranney's Irish terrier, « Old Nat. »

122

TWO HUNTERS IN THE WEST

present owner: Mr. Carl S. Dentzel [?],
Los Angeles, California
medium: pen and ink
size: 10×9.
collection:
Mr. Charles Lanman, Georgetown, D. C.
reference:
92, ii.

123

THREE FISHERMEN IN A SKIFF

present owner: Corcoran Gallery of Art,
Washington, D. C.
medium: pen and ink, heightened with white
size: $4^3/_4 \times 7$
collection:
Mr. Claude J. Ranney, Malvern, Pa.
references:
82, iv; 91.

49

124

DRAGOON WITH HIS CHARGER

present owner: Corcoran Gallery of Art,
Washington, D. C.
medium: pencil
size: $4^3/_4 \times 6^1/_2$

collection:
Mr. Claude J. Ranney, Malvern, Pa.
references:
82, iv; 91.

125

TOOTH EXTRACTION

present owner: Corcoran Gallery of Art,
Washington, D. C.
medium: wash drawing
size: $8^3/_4 \times 5^3/_8$
collection:
Mr. Claude J. Ranney, Malvern, Pa.
references:
82, iv; 91.

126

PIONEER CARAVAN

(Obverse)
present owner: Mr. Claude J. Ranney,
Malvern, Pennsylvania
medium: pencil
size: $5^3/_8 \times 8^3/_4$
comment:
Possibly related to No. 49.
This sketch and the following entries, Nos. 127-183,
are in the collection of the artist's grandson,
Mr. Claude J. Ranney, Malvern, Pennsylvania.
According to him, the initials « W. T. R. »
inscribed on many of these drawings were added
later by another hand.

127

FIGURE OF A MAN SITTING

(*Beggar*)
(Reverse of No. 126)
inscribed: « 50 Clinton Place ».

128

STUDY FOR 'FIRST NEWS OF THE BATTLE OF LEXINGTON'

medium: pencil
size: $7 \times 9^1/_8$
comment:
See No. 26.

129

STUDY FOR 'ON THE WING'

medium: pen and ink
size: $4 \times 5^7/_8$
comment:
See Nos. 45, 46.

130

STUDY FOR 'HUNTING WILD HORSES'

medium: black crayon heightened with white
size: $6^7/_8 \times 10$
comment:
See No. 21.

131

CALLING THE HOUNDS

medium: pencil
size: $5^3/_4 \times 7^3/_8$.

132

FRONTIER HORSE AUCTION

(Obverse)
medium: pencil
size: $8^3/_4 \times 11^5/_8$.

133

SLIGHT SKETCH OF GIST RESCUING WASHINGTON
FROM THE ALLEGHENY RIVER

(Reverse of No. 132)
medium: pencil
comment:
Related to No. 81.

134

GIST RESCUING WASHINGTON FROM
THE ALLEGHENY RIVER

medium: pencil
size: $8^1/_4 \times 10^1/_4$
comment:
Related to Nos. 81, 133.

135

RIVER SCENE WITH BOY FISHING

(Obverse)
medium: pencil heightened with white
size: 7×10.

136

SKETCH FOR 'FIRST NEWS OF THE BATTLE
OF LEXINGTON'

(Reverse of No. 135)
medium: pencil
comment:
See No. 26.

137

DUCK SHOOTERS

medium: pencil
size: $7^1/_2 \times 10^7/_8$.

138

THE PRANKSTER

medium: pencil
size: $6^7/_8 \times 7^3/_4$.

139

COAST SCENE WITH TWO FIGURES

medium: pen and ink
size: $5^5/_8 \times 5^3/_8$.

140

WASHINGTON WITH SOLDIERS

medium: pencil, pen and ink
size: $6^1/_8 \times 7^1/_2$.

141

THREE BOATS ON THE BEACH

medium: pencil heightened with white
size: 7×10.

142

LUNCH ON THE ROCKS

medium: pencil
size: $5^1/_2 \times 7^1/_2$.

143

MEXICAN WAR DRUMMER

medium: pencil
size: $3 \times 4^1/_8$.

144

SKETCHES OF PINES

medium: pencil
size: $6^1/_4 \times 8$.

145

STUDY OF A HORSE

(Obverse)
medium: brown crayon
size: 8×10.

146

STUDY OF FARMER WITH STONE SLED
AND MAN GESTURING

(Reverse of No. 145)
medium: pencil.

147

STUDY OF TWO OAK TREES

medium: pencil
size: $8^5/_8 \times 7$.

148

STUDY FOR 'THE RETREAT'

medium: pen and ink
size: $6^1/_2 \times 9^1/_2$
comment:
See No. 51.

149

COUNTRY BRIDGE NEAR MIDDLETOWN, CONN.

medium: pencil heightened with white
size: $9^1/_2 \times 14^3/_8$
signed: « Ranney » and inscribed with title
comment:
Possibly associated with No. 3.

150

LANDSCAPE WITH TREES AND ROCKS

(Obverse)
medium: pencil
size: $8^3/_8 \times 12^1/_2$.

151

SLIGHT LANDSCAPE SKETCH

(Reverse of No. 150)
medium: pencil.

152

WEEPING WILLOW

medium: pencil
size: $8^7/_8 \times 13^3/_4$.

153

A BONE OF CONTENTION

(Obverse)
medium: pencil
size: $5^3/_8 \times 8^3/_4$
inscribed with title, l. c.

154

SKETCH OF A YOUNG WOMAN

(Reverse of No. 153)
medium: pencil.

155

STUDY FOR 'ADVICE ON THE PRAIRIE'

(Obverse)
medium: pencil
size: $5^3/_8 \times 8^3/_4$
comment:
See Nos. 68, 69.

156

HAULING THE NET

(Reverse of No. 155)
medium: pencil.

157

STUDY OF A HORSE

medium: pencil heightened with white
size: 7×10.

158

GEORGE WASHINGTON CONVERSING WITH A WOMAN

medium: watercolor

size: $9^1/_2 \times 9^3/_4$.

159

GIRL WITH BIRD

medium: pencil

size: 6×5.

160

THE AMATEURS, and A TASTE FOR PORK

medium: pencil

size: $8^3/_4 \times 5^3/_8$.

Both sketches on obverse; titles so inscribed.

161

DOG SLEEPING

medium: pencil

size: $3^1/_2 \times 5^1/_4$

comment:

See No. 121.

162

LANDSCAPE WITH HORSEMAN

medium: pencil

size: $7^1/_4 \times 10^1/_4$.

163

HEAD OF A MAN

medium: pencil

size: $8^5/_8 \times 7$.

164

TREE

medium: pencil

size: $7^1/_2 \times 6^3/_4$.

165

'WEEKLY REVEILLE'

medium: pencil

size: $3^1/_2 \times 12$

comment:

Lettering probably for a periodical masthead.

166

FRANKLIN IN PHILADELPHIA

medium: pencil

size: $8^3/_8 \times 6^3/_4$.

167

TWO TREES

(Obverse)

medium: colored crayons

size: $12^1/_8 \times 9^1/_4$.

168

SKETCHES FOR DRAWING WITH THE STONE SLED

(Reverse of No. 167).

169

TREE WITH RAIL FENCE

(Obverse)

medium: pencil

size: $12^1/_4 \times 9^1/_4$.

170

SKETCH OF COWS DRINKING FROM A WELL SWEEP

(Reverse of No. 169).

171

FIELD WITH TREES

(Obverse)

medium: colored crayons

size: $12^1/_8 \times 9^1/_4$.

172

STUDY FOR FARMER WITH STONE SLED

(Reverse of No. 171)

medium: pencil.

173

STUDY OF ROCKS

(Obverse)

medium: black crayon heightened with white

size: $7^7/_8 \times 10$.

174

COMPOSITION

(Reverse of No. 173)

medium: pencil

175

LANDSCAPE WITH STREAM

medium: pencil heightened with white

size: $7 \times 10^1/_8$.

176

HEAD OF A MAN WITH GLASSES ON FOREHEAD

medium: pencil

size: $6^3/_8 \times 3^1/_4$.

177

STUDY OF A BARE TREE

medium: pencil

size: $13 \times 10^3/_4$.

178

TWO SKETCHES OF A MAN POLING

medium: pencil

size: $10^7/_8 \times 7^1/_2$

comment:
Possibly a study for WASHINGTON AND GIST
CROSSING THE ALLEGHENY RIVER, see Nos. 81, 133.

179

STUDY OF AN OLD TREE

medium: pencil
size: 7×11.

180

MEN WITH GUNS

medium: pencil.

181

MAN WITH PITCHFORK

medium: pencil.

182

SKETCH OF A WOMAN AND BOY

medium: pencil.
comment:
Possibly the artist's wife and their son, William.

183

SKETCH OF A SLUICE GATE

medium: pencil

184

THE ARTIST'S WIFE READING IN BED

medium: watercolor
size: 6³/₄×6.

PART III

ATTRIBUTED TO RANNEY; COPIES AFTER RANNEY; PRINTS AFTER RANNEY, DOUBTFUL WORKS, PROBABLY NOT BY RANNEY; ASSOCIATIONAL MATERIAL ATTRIBUTED TO RANNEY

185

WASHINGTON RALLYING THE AMERICANS
AT THE BATTLE OF PRINCETON

present owner: Private Collection
medium: oil
size: 25×30
exhibitions:
Samuel Freeman Auction Room, Philadelphia,
March, 1938, No. 32; Kennedy and Co., N.Y.,
« Life of Washington in Prints and Paintings, » Feb., 1945
collection:
Kennedy Galleries, N.Y.
reference:
78, iii
comment:
Possibly another version of his Princeton work (No. 28).
Contains many passages which are reminiscent
of the work of Ranney.
In some ways, this is a more interesting version.

COPIES AFTER RANNEY

186

MARION CROSSING THE PEDEE

present owner: Argosy Gallery, New York
medium, support: oil on canvas
size: 31×46
comment:
The artist of this copy has not been identified.
See No. 56.

187

MARION CROSSING THE PEDEE

present owner: Florence Museum,
Florence, South Carolina
inscribed, l. r.: « MARION CROSSING THE PEDEE. /
ARNOLD pinxit / 1857. »
exhibitions:
Louisiana State University Library,
Baton Rouge, La., « Louisiana Paintings
of the Nineteenth Century, » Oct.-Nov., 1959, No. 6

collection:
Mr. and Mrs. W. E. Groves, New Orleans, La.

reference:
115

comment:
The artist of this copy after Ranney's work (No. 56)
was Edward Arnold (1824/26-1866), who did historical,
marine, portrait, landscape and sign painting.
He was born in Heilbronn, Würtemberg, Germany,
and worked in New Orleans from about 1853
until his death. Perhaps his best known
painting is the BATTLE OF PORT HUDSON in the collection
of the United States National Museum. See No. 56.

188

THE TRAPPER'S LAST SHOT

present owner: Location unknown
size: 23×31

exhibitions:
Parke-Bernet Galleries, N.Y.,
March, 1954, No. 438

collection:
Mr. John S. Clark, Jr. and Agnes Clark,
Philadelphia and Alcescot House, Alcescot,
Oxfordshire, England

reference:
126, ii

comment:
Described in the Parke-Bernet *Catalogue* as

> A trapper with a gun, astride a brown
> horse standing in the middle of a pond,
> looking toward the left, where a group
> of Indians is approaching....
> The painting is accompanied by the well-known
> Currier and Ives colored lithograph,
> and also by the steel engraving by T. D. Booth,
> Cincinnati. It is said to be the original
> from which the reproductions were made;
> but while we have retained
> the attribution to Ranney, it must be added
> that there are differences of opinion
> as to whether it is by the painter's own hand.
> It will be noted that it lacks the signature which
> appears on the saddle in the print.

189

THE TRAPPER'S LAST SHOT

present owner: Mr. Robert B. Honeyman, Jr.,
New York

medium, support: oil on canvas
size: c. 18×25
inscribed, l.r.: « W. Ranney »

comment:
Probably a contemporary copy after
the Booth engraving. See Nos. 41, 42, 197.

190

THE TRAPPER'S LAST SHOT

present owner: Argosy Gallery, New York.

191

THE TRAPPER'S LAST SHOT

present owner: Mr. Wayman C. Park,
Bellflower, California

medium, support: oil on canvas
Canvas has Winsor & Newton, London, stencil on back

comment:
See Nos. 41, 42, 197.

192

THE TRAPPER'S LAST SHOT

present owner: Location unknown

comment:
See Nos. 41, 42, 197. Most of the copies seem
to have derived from the Booth engraving.

193

ON THE WING

present owner: Location unknown

comment:
A contributor to *The Crayon*, April, 1858,
while describing art conditions in Chicago, stated:

> ... In Cooke & Co.'s bookstore is for
> sale Nahl's painting, « Lady with Paroquet »
> (dated 1850), in which much gay-colored
> still-life is carefully rendered; price asked $2000.
> The only painting besides this is a copy
> from Ranney's « On the Wing, »
> by Wilson, of Philadelphia; price $1500....

The prices for these works, if true,
are surprising. Possibly the artist referred
to for the copy after Ranney was Jeremy Wilson,
a portrait and landscape painter working
in Philadelphia in the 1850's. See also Comment, No. 46.

194

ON THE WING — WILD DUCK SHOOTING

present owner: Mr. Hermann Warner Williams, Jr.,
Washington, D.C.

collection:
Dr. Charles Porter, Maryland.

ENGRAVINGS AFTER RANNEY,
OR ASSOCIATED WITH HIS WORK

195

DANIEL BOONE'S FIRST VIEW OF KENTUCKY

size: 5¹/₂×8

comment:
Steel engraving by Alfred Jones (1819-1900).
Commissioned by the American Art-Union
and printed in their *Bulletin* for May, 1850,
facing page 17. See No. 38.
From the collection of the New York Public Library.
Jones was born in Liverpool, England,
and came to America as a young man,

settling in New York, where he worked chiefly
as a banknote engraver, but was also well-known
for his engravings after works by American artists.

196

BOONE AND HIS COMPANIONS. – FIRST VIEW OF KENTUCKY

comment:
A wood engraving by Nathaniel Orr, New York,
which appeared as the frontispiece in William Henry
Bogart's *Daniel Boone, and the Hunters of Kentucky,*
1854. While this is not a direct copy of Ranney's work,
or the Jones engraving, enough similarities
exist in the arrangement of the figures and setting,
in reverse, to warrant an assumption
that it was probably inspired by Ranney's earlier
rendition. See No. 38. Orr was one
of the more prolific wood engravers of his day.
His illustrations appeared in a large number
of books and magazines.

197

THE TRAPPER'S LAST SHOT

size: $23^1/_2 \times 18$
inscribed on saddle: « W. Ranney - 50 »
comment:
A steel line engraving by T. Dwight Booth,
printed by J. M. Emerson of New York,
for the Western Art-Union as their distribution print
to each member of 1850. The *Transactions of the Western
Art-Union for the Year 1850* stated on page 15,
it was « ... a representation of a scene in the far West,
of peculiar interest, and it has been engraved
by our fellow-citizen, Booth, in a style which will establish
his reputation in this branch of art. »
Booth worked as an engraver between 1830 and 1857
in New York, Cincinnati and Chicago.
He is listed in the Cincinnati *Directory*
for 1849-1850, 1850-1851, and 1853.
This illustration was photographed from the print
in the collection of Mr. Robert B. Honeyman, Jr.,
New York. See No. 41.

198

ON THE WING

size: $7^1/_2 \times 5$
comment:
A steel line engraving by Charles Burt (1823-1892),
commissioned by the American Art-Union,
and published in the *Bulletin* for October, 1850,
facing page 113. From the collection
of the New York Public Library. See No. 45.
Burt was born in Edinburgh, Scotland, and worked
in the New York area from 1850.
He was regarded as one of our foremost engravers.

199

MARION CROSSING THE PEDEE

size: $10 \times 7^1/_2$
comment:
A steel line engraving by Charles Burt,
printed by J. Dalton, and commissioned
by the American Art-Union for the series

of prints entitled « The Gallery of American Art, »
which was distributed to each member of 1851.
From the collection of the New York Public Library.
See No. 56.

200

THE SCOUTING PARTY

size: $4^1/_2 \times 7^1/_4$
comment:
A wood engraving from a drawing by William R. Miller
after Ranney's painting (No. 60), engraved
by [James H. ?] Richardson, for the American Art-Union.
It was published in the *Bulletin* for September 1,
1851, page 89.

DOUBTFUL WORKS, PROBABLY NOT BY RANNEY

201

THE BATTLE OF PRINCETON, NEW JERSEY

present owner: Location unknown
comment:
Formerly attributed to William Ranney.
Now attributed to John R. Chapin (1823-after 1907).
Photograph from the Frick Art Reference Library,
which received it from The Old Print Shop, New York.

202

WASHINGTON AT THE BATTLE OF MONMOUTH, JUNE 28, 1778

present owner: Chicago Historical Society
reference:
73
comment:
A brief note in the *American Heritage* pointed out that

> The victory at Monmouth was the work not
> only of Washington (center, receiving captured colors)
> but also of the great drillmaster, von Steuben....
> This anonymous early Nineteenth-Century painting
> gets in everything, including Molly Pitcher
> in a straw hat (far right)
> [sic; Molly Pitcher, if it is she, is probably
> the woman standing by the cannon on the hillside
> in the background, below the American flag]....

The general design of the central group of figures
is so similar to that found in No. 201,
as to suggest that one derived directly from the other.
The differences in titles should not be difficult
to suggest an explanation. An examination
of the Frick photograph, No. 201,
reveals that the hillside in the background,
with Molly Pitcher at the cannon, has been omitted.
Also, the lack of many other details found
in the Chicago painting, and the suggestion of a less
competent hand technically in the Frick photograph
of that painting might give some credence
to an assumption that the latter work was taken either
from the Chicago example or, possibly, No. 203,
and if the present title is correct,
the artist (Chapin ?) simply transformed
it into a rendition of the battle of Princeton,
with the death of Mercer taking place at the right.

203

WASHINGTON AT THE BATTLE OF MONMOUTH, JUNE 28, 1778

present owner: Mr. Edward T. Harrison, Jr.,
Leesburg, Virginia

comment:

A more accomplished work technically than No. 201,
and so close in design to the Chicago painting
in all aspects that a fair question might be raised
as to which painting followed the other,
or if, perhaps, they were not executed by the same hand.
Certain passages in the rendition of the foliage suggest
Ranney's manner, but the horses do not have
his authority, nor has any indication been discovered
in contemporary or other sources that Ranney ever
painted this theme.
A MOLL [sic] PITCHER AT THE BATTLE OF MONMOUTH
by « Miller » was listed in an auction advertisement
in the *New York Herald*, December 16, 1857.
She is such an insignificant figure in both paintings
that it would seem unlikely that there would be any
connection; however, the name of the artist might
offer a possible clue.

204

FRANCIS MARION AT BLACK MINGOL CREEK

present owner: Mrs. H. S. Green,
Worcester, Massachusetts

comment:
No record of this title or theme having been
painted by Ranney has been discovered
in contemporary sources. John R. Chapin
has also been suggested
as the possible artist of this work.

205

PIONEERS

comment:

In Cowdrey and Williams' monograph
on *William Sidney Mount*, 1944, this painting
is described in Appendix A, page 36.

> Works Incorrectly Attributed to Mount...
> (IX) PIONEERS. Oil on canvas, 29 in. x
> 36 in. Signed on barrel in wagon on left:
> J [?] W. MOUN [?] - [?] The painting shows
> a covered wagon on the left, and a tent
> on the right before which a group of six figures,
> under a sunset sky, are gathered
> around a campfire.
> NOTE: This picture may possibly show the influence
> of William S. Mount in the handling of the foliage
> in the left foreground, otherwise it is
> not like his style of painting.
> It is certainly mid-nineteenth century American
> and bears a resemblance to the work
> of William Ranney. The partially illegible
> inscription which was not apparent until
> the painting was cleaned in 1942 would
> appear to be contemporaneous.
> *present owner*: Harry Stone, New York.

A possibility exists that this might have
been another painting by Ranney finished by Mount,
but until further information is uncovered it must
remain doubtful.

206

WILLIAM RANNEY

present owner: National Academy of Design,
New York
verified date: c. 1850
medium, support: oil on canvas
size: 30×25
exhibitions:
National Academy of Design, N. Y.,
« Selection of Paintings from the Permanent Collection
of the National Academy of Design, » Dec. 4-31, 1934
comment:
The original portrait of William Ranney,
said to have been painted by James Bogle,
c. 1850, was extensively damaged by fire in the early
1900's or around 1940. It was not signed or dated.
The painting noted here, No. 206, is a copy,
also in the collection of the National Academy of Design,
painted by an unknown artist.
James Bogle, N. A. (c. 1817-1873 or 1878)
was a portrait and genre painter.
Before 1843, he worked in Charleston and Baltimore.
From 1843 until his death, he resided in New York.
He was made an Academician in 1861. His brother,
Robert Bogle (c. 1817-after 1860) was also
a portrait painter who worked mainly in the South.

207

WILLIAM RANNEY PAINTING

'THE HALT ON THE PLAINS'
present owner: Miss Margaret Ranney,
Union City, New Jersey
verified date: c. 1856-1857
medium: Wash Drawing
size: 30×24
comment:
The artist of this interesting portrait has not been
identified, although it is tempting to suggest certain
possibilities, such as Charles Loring Elliott,
Edwin White, or William Sidney Mount.
Perhaps the smaller painting resting against the base
of the easel was a preparatory sketch
(see *Fund Catalogue*, No. 93). See also No. 86
for a comparison with the large painting.

208

Business Card of William Ranney.

From the collection of Mr. Claude J. Ranney,
Malvern, Pennsylvania.

209

signature: « William Ranney / West hoboken,
N. Jerse[y] / 1854. » From the collection
of Mr. Claude J. Ranney, Malvern, Pennsylvania.

210

Photograph of the Ranney home, West Hoboken,
New Jersey. From *50th Anniversary of the Incorporation
of the Town of West Hoboken, N. J.*, 1911.

APPENDIX

THE RANNEY FUND EXHIBITION AND SALE

The Ranney Fund exhibition and sale was held at the National Academy of Design, New York, during the month of December, 1858 (see pp. 11-13). A valuable source of information regarding this event is the scrapbook volume entitled *The Ranney Collection*, in the collection of the New York Historical Society. All of the material quoted or otherwise referred to in this Appendix derives from this source, unless otherwise stated. *The Ranney Collection* volume contains a sales catalogue, two printed notices by the Fund committee, a ticket to the exhibition (with Nason B. Collins' initials inscribed on it), and various clippings pertaining to the affair or to the artist, mostly from contemporary newspapers.

Prior to the exhibition, a printed form was sent by the committee to various collectors known to have pictures by Ranney, of which the following is an example.

New-York, Nov. 19, 1858.

Jos. Moreau, Esq. [inscribed]

Dear Sir, –

The Artists of New-York will open an Exhibition of Mr. Ranney's Pictures, December 1st, together with pieces painted by themselves, which they have given to be sold for the benefit of Mr. Ranney's widow, at the close of the exhibition.

Hearing that you are the possessor of one of Mr. Ranney's pictures, the Committee take the liberty of requesting you to loan them the said picture to exhibit with the others, they paying all expenses of transportation, & c.

The funds arising from the exhibition will, of course, be appropriated for the benefit of Mrs. Ranney, who, we are sorry to say, is in need of the sympathy and help of all her friends.

If you will send an answer as soon as possible after receipt of this, you will much oblige the Committee.

Direct to

N. B. Collins
23 Wall St.　　　　[inscribed]
N. Y.

P. S. – Notice will be given you where to send the pictures, after receipt of your answer.

The exhibition opened on Monday, December 6, 1858, in the rooms of the National Academy of Design on Tenth Street, near Broadway. Admission was tenty-five cents and exhibition hours were from 9:00 A.M. until 10:00 P.M.

A statement by the commitee regarding the purposes of the event was included with the printed *Catalogue*.

> A number of the friends of the late William Ranney, being desirous of expressing in some way their sense of his abilities as an Artist, and his character as a man, decided upon offering a testimonial to his memory, which, at the same time, might be of some permanent value to his bereaved family. The Artists generally, therefore, of the City of New-York, by a mutual understanding, agreed to contribute some works of their own pencils, which being added to the Sketches left by Mr. Ranney, at his decease, might form a collection sufficiently various for an interesting Exhibition, with the ultimate view of selling all these productions at Auction, at the close of the Exhibition. The proceeds to be disposed of as the Artists may direct, for the benefit of the widow and children of the deceased Artist. With this intention the present collection of Pictures has been formed, and it is now respectfully recommended to the attention of the public, not only giving them a chance to procure some works of Mr. Ranney's, which, of course, as every year passes by, becomes more valuable, but also brings before them a collection of our own Artists' Pictures, of real merit, and any buyer can feel, as he looks on the picture after it is purchased, that in becoming a possessor of it, he was helping along a noble act of charity.

The exhibition contained 212 works, of which 108 were by Ranney. The names of many well-known artists of that day, as well as a number of the lesser-known, are found among the remaining 104 items, all of which were contributed. Ranney's work was not listed separately, but interspersed among that of the other artists.

The sale was conducted on the evenings of December 20 and 21, beginning at 7:30 P.M. The following list of works by William Ranney was compiled from the *Catalogue of Paintings to Be Sold for the Benefit of the Ranney Fund*. The original *Catalogue* numbers were utilized, and entries by artists other than Ranney have not been included. In addition, this copy of the *Catalogue* had been carefully ruled in pencil in order that a notation, recorded in ink, could be made before and after each item, pertaining to the price paid and the buyer's last name. In the list which follows, this information will be found in brackets. At the bottom of each page of the *Catalogue* a total was made of the sales and, on the last page, the sum total for the whole auction was computed. In all probability, this was the *Catalogue* used to keep a record during the sale's progress, perhaps by the merchant, Nason B. Collins.

There is little else in the manner of descriptive information for the various works listed and, lacking additional factual data, it would be impossible at this time to make a valid attempt at identifying and classifying most of the items according to their exact place in the artist's *oeuvre*. Many were undoubtedly preparatory sketches and working drawings from his studio. However, judging by the higher prices paid for a few, there must have been some major paintings by Ranney included. Tentative associations, mainly on the basis of title similarities, have been made in Part I. In spite of the present nebulous state of knowledge regarding the Fund sale items, there can be no question but what these works must be considered as a valid and necessary part of his total effort.

1. SKETCH FROM NATURE — AMERICAN SCENERY
   [17.50; Russell].
3. COW
   [10; Jarvis].
5. DOCK LEAVES
   [5; Brady].
7. OLD-FASHIONED OVEN
   [10; Jarvis].
9. AUTUMN — A SKETCH
   [10; Wood].
11. THE COW SHED
   [5; Johnson].
13. HORSES
   [27.50; O. Richards].
15. STUDY FROM NATURE
   [5; Barry].
17. HORSE'S HEAD
   [4; Booth].
18. COW'S HEAD
   [16; Putnam].
20. SKETCH FROM NATURE OF GRASS
   [4; Barry].
22. SKETCH FROM NATURE
   [8; Menzies].
24. WOUNDED HOUND
   [21; Wood].
26. LAKE PISACO
   [15; Lord].
28. STUDY FOR LARGE PICTURE OF COW BOYS
   QUARRELLING OVER THEIR PLUNDER
   [22; Menzies].
30. STUDY OF A MULE
   [15; Kensett].
32. CATTLE REPOSING
   [17; Jarvis].
34. SKETCH FROM NATURE
   [8; Hoxie].
36. SETTER DOG
   [13; Walker].
38. A TRAPPER CROSSING THE MOUNTAINS
   [17; Walker].
40. ANIMALS
   [10; Bell].
42. ARTIST'S SHANTY, LAKE PISACO
   [6; Worth].
44. FINISHED SKETCH FROM NATURE
   [90; Menzies].
46. SKETCH FROM NATURE
   [40; Russell].
48. RECONNOITERING
   [15; Barry].
50. SALE OF MANHATTAN ISLAND TO THE DUTCH
   [26; Pepoon].
52. SKETCH FROM NATURE
   [9; Barry].
54. PRAIRIE ON FIRE
   [15; Walker].
56. TRAPPERS ON THE LOOKOUT
   [21; Walker].
58. A STUDY — BRADDOCK'S FUNERAL
   [16; Walker].
60. PORTRAIT OF A FAVORITE DOG
   [45; Jarvis].
62. HORSE
   [5; Wood].

63. STUDY FOR A LARGE PICTURE —
   REVOLUTIONARY ENLISTMENT
   [26; Pepoon].
65. SAM
   [7.50; Williams].
67. CATTLE AND HORSES
   [13; Barry].
69. TRAPPERS SCOUTING
   [6; Work].
71. A GOAT
   [8; Wood].
73. HORSE
   [6; Briggs].
75. ENLISTING DURING THE REVOLUTIONARY WAR
   [100; Brady].
77. NEWFOUNDLAND DOG
   [21; Swan].
79. RABBIT HUNTING
   [21; Eastburn].
81. TORIES WITH A PRISONER
   [75; Pepoon].
83. THE WESTERN GIRL
   [21; N. Collins * Re-sold for 40 on the 21st.
   Second buyer not recorded].
85. HAYSTACK AND CATTLE
   [58; Howe].
87. STUDY FOR HIS LAST PICTURE
   [12.50; Wood].
89. STUDY FOR PICTURE, WASHINGTON CROSSING
   THE SUSQUEHANNAH
   [17; Wood].
91. RECONNOITERING
   [5; Wood].
93. SKETCH FOR PICTURE, HALT ON THE PRAIRIE
   [8; Wood].
95. MULES' HEADS
   [21; Wood].
96. TORIES WITH A PRISONER
   [8.50; Wood]
97. TRAPPERS
   [5; Wood].
98. SLY PEEP
   [9; Wood].
100. COWS
   [30; Spencer].
104. WOLVES AND DEER
   [13; Havens].
105. COWS
   [10; Howe].
107. SKETCH OF AN INDIAN FIGHT
   [5; Howe].
109. SKETCH OF FIGURES
   [3; W. Johnson].
114. GOAT
   [3.50; Perkins].
116. ERRAND BOY
   [2.50; Warner].
118. DUCK SHOOTING
   [27; Wood].
120. WASHINGTON AND HIS LADY VISITING SICK
   SOLDIERS, (SKETCH FOR LARGE PICTURE)
   [3; Brown].
122. SKETCH FROM NATURE
   [11; Howe].

124. COW'S HEAD
[5; Havens].
126. LOADING UP
[12; Walker].
132 LANDSCAPE WITH COWS
[27; Sullivan].
134. SKETCH OF TREES
[5; Dodge].
136. THE STANDARD BEARER
[4; Wood].
138. EXPRESS RIDER
[12; N. Collins].
140. DOWNFALL OF MONARCHY
[9; O'Brian].
142. COWS
[5; Havens].
144. THE BARN YARD
[25; Riggs].
146. SKETCH FROM NATURE
[9; Howe].
148. CATTLE
[17; Swan].
150. WATER COLOR DRAWING
[4; Walker].
152. THE FRESHET
[14; N. Collins].
153. RADDISH [sic] GIRL
[11; Hurlburt].
156. HORSE'S HEAD
[10; Hurlburt].
159. SCOUTS ON THE PRAIRIE
[62.50; Wood].
161. THE WOUNDED SCOUT
[25; Walker].
164. MUSK RAT HUNTING
[60; Hurlburt].
166. WAITING FOR THE FERRY
[15; Riggs].
168. SNIPE SHOOTING, (very fine)
[150; Wood].
170. THE TRAPPER'S HALT, (very fine)
[340; Dr. Bissell].
172. BARN YARD
[16; Pepoon].
174. STUDY OF PICTURE, VIRGINIA WEDDING
[30; Menzies].

176. STUDY FOR LARGE PICTURE, DANIEL BOON
AND PARTY
[6; Walker].
178. LAST SHOT
[50; Brooking].
180. SOLDIERS IN THE SNOW
[2; Brooking].
182. RABBIT HUNTING
[4; Riggs].
184. DOGS
[8; Eastman].
186. DEAD HORSE
[4; Endicott]
188. SNIPE SHOOTING
[3; Riggs].
190. SKETCH
[2.50; Riggs].
191. SCHOOL BOYS
[6; Eastman]. *105449*
192. DROVER'S HALT
[5; Waite].
194. RETURN FROM HUNTING
[6; Burt].
196. DEER HUNTING ON THE LAKES
[7; Eastman].
197. PEN AND INK DRAWING
[5; Waite].
198. PEN AND INK DRAWING
[5; Riggs].
199. PEN AND INK DRAWING
[4; Brooking].
200. SKETCH
[7; Waite].
201. SOLDIERS FORDING A RIVER
[2.50; Riggs].
202. WAGON ON THE SNOW
[3; Anderson].
203. FISHERMAN
[6; Riggs].
204. DOG AND DUCK
[2; Ross].
205. DYING HORSE
[2; Anderson].
206. HUNTER WITH GAME
[3; Anderson].
207. CATTLE
[6; Riggs].

BIBLIOGRAPHY

I. BOOKS

1. Adams, Charles Collard, *Middletown Upper Houses*, New York, 1908.
2. Baker, W. S., *American Engravers and Their Works*, Philadelphia, 1875.
3. Barker, Virgil, *American Painting*, New York, 1951.
4. Benjamin, S. G. W., *Art in America*, New York, 1880.
5. Bland, Jane C., *Currier & Ives*, New York, 1931.
6. Bogart, W. H., *Daniel Boone, and the Hunters of Kentucky*, Auburn and Buffalo, 1854.
7. Catlin, Geo., *Letters and Notes on the Manners, Customs, and Condition of the North American Indians...*, London, 1841, 2 Vols.
8. Clark, Eliot, *History of the National Academy of Design 1825-1953*, New York, 1954.
9. Conningham, Frederic A., *Currier & Ives Prints*, New York, 1949.
10. Cowdrey, Mary Bartlett, *American Academy of Fine Arts and American Art-Union*, New York, 1953, 2 Vols.
11. — — —, *National Academy of Design Exhibition Record 1826-1860*, New York, 1943, 2 Vols.
12. — — —, and Hermann Warner Williams, Jr., *William Sidney Mount, 1807-1868. An American Painter.* New York, 1944.
13. Crane, Aimée (Ed.), *Portrait of America*, New York, 1945.
14. Crosby, Nathan, *Annual Obituary Notices of Eminent Persons, Who Have Died in the United States, For 1857*, Boston, 1858.
15. Cummings, Thomas S., *Historic Annals of the National Academy of Design*, Philadelphia, 1865.
16. Darlington, William M., *Christopher Gist's Journals*, Pittsburgh, 1893.
17. Dumas, Malone (Ed.), *Dictionary of American Biography*, New York, 1935, Vol. XV. [William Howe Downes].
18. Egbert, Donald D., *Princeton Portraits*, Princeton, 1947.
19. Fielding, Mantle, *Dictionary of American Painters, Sculptors And Engravers*, Philadelphia, [c. 1925].
20. Filson, John, *The Discovery, Settlement and present State of Kentucke...* Wilmington, 1784.
21. Flint, Timothy, *Biographical Memoir of Daniel Boone, the First Settler of Kentucky*, Cincinnati, 1833.
22. French, H. W., *Art and Artists in Connecticut*, Boston and New York, 1879.
23. [Frost, John] *Pictorial Life of General Marion*, Philadelphia, 1847.
24. Groce, George C., and David H. Wallace, *The New-York Historical Society's Dictionary of Artists in America*, New Haven, 1957.
25. Harrison, Gabriel, *A History of the Progress of the Drama, Music and the Fine Arts in the City of Brooklyn*, Brooklyn, 1884.
26. Hartmann, Sadakichi, *A History of American Art*, Boston, 1901, Vol. I.
27. Herringshaw, Thomas W., *Herringshaw's Encyclopedia of American Biography of the Nineteenth Century*, Chicago, 1904.
28. — — —, *Herringshaw's National Library of American Biography*, Chicago, 1914, Vol. IV.
29. Irving, Washington, *Life of Washington*, New York, 1855, Vol. I.
30. James, William D., *A Sketch of the Life of Brig. Gen. Francis Marion and a History of His Brigade*, Marietta, 1948 [A. S. Salley, Ed.].
31. Ketchum, Richard M., (Ed.), *The American Heritage Book of the Revolution*, New York, 1958.
32. Lanman, Charles, *Haphazard Personalities*, Boston, 1886.
33. Larkin, Oliver W., *Art and Life in America*, New York, 1949.
34. — — —, in *Encyclopedia of World Art*, New York, Toronto and London, 1959, Vol. I.
35. Lossing, Benson J., *Eminent Americans...* New York, 1857.
36. Mallett, Daniel T., *Mallett's Index of Artists*, New York, 1948.
37. Marcy, Randolph B., *The Prairie Traveler...* New York, 1863.
38. McCracken, Harold, *Portrait of the Old West*, New York, Toronto and London, 1952.
39. Miller, Dorothy, *The Life and Work of David G. Blythe*, Pittsburgh, 1950.
40. Monro, Isabel S., and Kate M. Monro, *Index to Reproductions of American Paintings*, New York, 1948.
41. Montgomery, Walter, (Ed.), *American Art and American Art Collections*, Boston, 1889, Vol. I.
42. Moore, Horatio N., *The Life and Times of Gen. Francis Marion*, Philadelphia, 1845.
43. *Ornaments of Memory...*, New York, 1856 and 1857.
44. Parkman, Jr., Francis, *The California and Oregon Trail...*, New York, 1849.
45. Peck, John M., *Life of Daniel Boone*, Boston, 1847. [Jared Sparks, Ed., *The Library of American Biography*, Second Series, Vol. XIII].
46. Peters, Harry T., *Currier & Ives...*, New York, 1931, Vol. II.
47. Richardson, Edgar P., *American Romantic Painting*, New York, 1944.
48. — — —, *Painting in America*, New York, 1956.
49. Roberts, Kenneth, *The Battle of Cowpens...*, New York, 1958.
50. Rutledge, Anna W., *Cumulative Record of Exhibition Catalogues, The Pennsylvania Academy of the Fine Arts 1800-1870...*, Philadelphia, 1955.
51. Sheldon, G. W., *Hours with Art and Artists*, New York, 1882.
52. Sherman, Frederick F., *Early American Painting*, New York, 1932.
53. Smith, Ralph C., *A Biographical Index of American Artists*, Baltimore, 1930.
54. Strahan, Edward, (Ed.) [Earl Shinn], *Art Treasures of America*, Philadelphia, [c. 1880] Vols. II-III.
55. Taft, Robert, *Artists and Illustrators of the Old West 1850-1900*, New York, 1953.
56. Thieme, Ulrich and Felix Becker, *Allgemeines Lexikon der Bildenden Künstler*, Leipzig, 1934, Vol. XXVIII.
57. Trollope, Frances M., *Domestic Manners of the Americans*, New York, 1904.
58. Tuckerman, Henry T., *Book of the Artists, American Artist Life*, New York, 1867.

59. Turner, Frederick J., *The Frontier in American History*, New York, 1920 and 1950.

59a. Walton, John, *John Filson of Kentucke*, Lexington, 1956.

60. Weitenkampf, F., *American Graphic Art*, New York, 1912 and 1924.

61. Wilmot-Buxton, H. J., and S. R. Koehler, *English Painters*, London, 1883.

62. Wilson, James G., (Ed.), *The Memorial History of the City of New-York*, New York, 1892-93, Vols. I, IV [F. Weitenkampf].

63. — — —, and John Fiske, (Eds.), *Appletons' Cyclopaedia of American Biography*, New York, 1888, Vol. V [F. Weitenkampf].

64. Wood, William and Ralph H. Gabriel, *The Winning of Freedom*, New Haven, 1927, Vol. VI [*The Pageant of America Series*].

65. Young, William, *Lights and Shadows of New York Picture Galleries*, New York, 1864.

II. CATALOGUES, PERIODICALS, DIRECTORIES, PAMPHLETS

66. Adams, Charles C., *To the Gaylords and the Notts. Heirs to the Estates of William Nott, Jr., and John J. Nott*, Cromwell, 1911.

67. American Artist Association, Anderson Galleries, *Catalogue, Wanamaker Sale*, New York, 1936, p. 11.

68. — — —, *Sale of American Historical Paintings*, New York, 1938, p. 36.

American Art-Union, New York:

69. *Bulletin*:

   i. June 1, 1847, pp. 8, 9.
   ii. Sept. 15, 1847, pp. 8, 9.
   iii. Nov. 1, 1847, pp. 6, 7, 11.
   iv. Dec. 15, 1847, pp. 5, 6, 10.
   v. June 25, 1848, p. 9.
   vi. July 10, 1848, p. 9.
   vii. July 25, 1848, p. 8.
   viii. Aug. 12, 1848, p. 8.
   ix. Aug. 25, 1848, p. 9.
   x. Sept. 10, 1848, p. 9.
   xi. Sept. 25, 1848, p. 9.
   xii. Oct. 10, 1848, p. 9.
   xiii. Oct. 25, 1848, p. 9.
   xiv. Nov. 10, 1848, p. 10.
   xv. Nov. 25, 1848, p. 10.
   xvi. Dec. 10, 1848, pp. 10, 15.
   xvii. Dec. 25, 1848, pp. 11, 20, 23.
  xviii. April, 1849, p. 23.
   xix. May, 1849, p. 21.
   xx. June, 1849, p. 32.
   xxi. July, 1849, p. 31.
   xxii. Aug. 1849, pp. 29, 31, 43.
   xxiii. Sept. 1849, p. 34.
   xxiv. Oct. 1849, pp. 28, 37.
   xxv. Nov. 1849, pp. 18, 30, 38.
   xxvi. Dec. 1849, pp. 27, 35.
   xxvii. April 1, 1850, pp. 2, 15.
  xxviii. May, 1850, facing p. 17, pp. 21, 29.
   xxix. June, 1850, p. 45.
   xxx. July, 1850, p. 51.
   xxxi. Aug. 1850, p. 81.
   xxxii. Sept. 1850, pp. 87, 88.
  xxxiii. Oct. 1850, facing p. 113, p. 115.
  xxxiv. Nov. 1850, pp. 123, 138-9.
  xxxv. Dec. 1850, p. 144.
  xxxvi. Dec. 31, 1850, pp. 88, 167, 169, 172, 174.
  xxxvii. April 1, 1851, p. 17.
  xxxviii. May 1, 1851, p. 35.
  xxxix. June 1, 1851, p. 43.
   xl. Aug. 1, 1851, p. 85.
   xli. Sept. 1, 1851, pp. 85, 89.
   xlii. Oct. 1, 1851, p. v.
   xliii. Nov. 1, 1851, p. 135.
   xliv. Dec. 1, 1851, p. 153.
   xlv. Dec. 1851, Supplementary, pp. 5, 7, 8.

70. *Catalogues*: (Other than those appended to regular *Bulletin* issues.)

   i. *Catalogue of Works of Art, Purchased by the American Art Union, to Be Distributed by Lot among the Members at the Annual Meeting in December*, 1849, pp. 2, 5, 9.

   ii. *American Art-Union Distribution Catalogue*, December 21, 1849, pp. 2, 10.

  iii. *Catalogue of Pictures and Other Works of Art. The Property of the American Art-Union. To Be Sold at Auction by David Austen, Jr., at the Gallery...*, December, 1852, pp. 9, 13, 15.

  iv. *American Art-Union. Artists' Sale. John H. Austen, Auctioneer. Catalogue of Very Valuable and Choice Paintings, Recently selected from the studios of the most distinguished American and resident Artists, to be sold without reserve, at Auction...*, December 30, 1852, p. 10.

71. *Transactions*:

   i. *For the Year 1845*, pp. 27, 29.
   ii. *For the Year 1846*, pp. 31, 34.
  iii. *For the Year 1847*, pp. 32, 33, 39, 43, 49.
   iv. *For the Year 1848*, pp. 25, 57, 68, 72.
   v. *For the Year 1849*, pp. 41, 46.

72. *American Collector*:

   i. Sept. 1947, p. 18.
   ii. Oct. 1948, p. 15.

73. *American Heritage*, June, 1955, p. 3 and cover.

74. *American Quarterly*, Vol. 7, No. 2, 1955, p. 148.

75. Anderson Galleries, *Catalogue, Stokes Collection Sale*, New York, 1929, No. 78.

76. *50th Anniversary of the Incorporation of the Town of West Hoboken, N. J.*, 1911, n. p.

77. *Annual, Opening, and Concluding Addresses Delivered before the Maryland Institute for the Promotion of the Mechanic Arts, During the Annual Exhibition of the Institute, in 1848, 1849 and 1850*, Baltimore, [c. 1850].

78. *Antiques*:

   i. Jan. 1925, p. 11.
   ii. Jan. 1926, p. 24.
  iii. Feb. 1945, p. 76.
   iv. May, 1945, p. 260.
   v. Nov. 1952, p. 364.
   vi. Feb. 1953, p. 104.
   vii. Jan. 1956, p. 6.
  viii. June, 1959, p. 530.

79. *Art Digest*:

    i. Jan. 15, 1934, p. 15.
    ii. May 1, 1939, pp. 5-6.
    iii. April 15, 1942, p. 18.
    iv. May 1, 1945, p. 19.
    v. May 1, 1946, p. 5.
    vi. Sept. 15, 1947, pp. 2, 17.
    vii. Oct. 1, 1951, p. 9.
    viii. March, 1954, p. 34.

80. *Art in America*, Vol. 40, No. 1, 1952, p. 13.

81. *Art News*, Oct. 1947, p. 43.

82. *Art Quarterly*:

    i. Autumn, 1940, p. 372.
    ii. Spring, 1945, p. 144.
    iii. Spring, 1947, p. 154.
    iv. Spring, 1961, p. 97.

83. The Baltimore Museum of Art, *Shooting And Fishing In Art*, 1958, No. 22.

84. Benjamin, S. G. W., « The Corcoran Gallery of Art, » *The Century Magazine*, Sept. 1882, pp. 815-25.

85. The Museum of Fine Arts, Boston:

    i. *M. and M. Karolik Collection of American Paintings 1815 to 1865*, Cambridge, 1949, pp. 462-64, pl. 206.
    ii. *American Paintings, 1815-1865*, Boston, 1956, pp. 90, 92.
    iii. *Sport in American Art*, Boston, 1944, p. 18.

86. *Catalogue. The Collection of Paintings, Drawings, and Statuary, the Property of John Taylor Johnston, Esq., to Be Sold at Auction*, New York, 1876, p. 79.

87. *Catalogue of Paintings and Other Works of Art, Presented to the Metropolitan Fair in Aid of the U. S. Sanitary Commission, to Be Sold at Auction*, New York, 1864, p. 5.

88. Cincinnati, City Directories:

    i. 1849-50, p. 39.
    ii. 1850-51, p. 38.
    iii. 1853, p. 43.

89. *Circular of the Mechanics' Institute of the City of New-York...*, New York, 1836.

The Corcoran Gallery of Art, Washington, D. C.:

90. *Catalogues*:

    i. 1857, p. 9 [Charles Lanman].
    ii. 1874, p. 5.
    iii. 1875, p. 43.
    iv. 1878, p. 57 [William MacLeod].
    v. 1887, p. 63 [Idem.].
    vi. 1888, p. 64 [Idem.].
    vii. 1892, p. 46.
    viii. 1897, pp. 69, 159.
    ix. 1904, p. 29.
    x. 1905, p. 29.
    xi. 1908, p. 76.
    xii. 1909, p. 76.
    xiii. 1911, p. 76.
    xiv. 1913, p. 76.
    xv. 1915, p. 76.
    xvi. 1917, p. 80.
    xvii. 1919, p. 77.
    xviii. 1920, p. 74.
    xix. 1920, p. 45.
    xx. 1926, p. 69.
    xxi. 1939, p. 79.
    xxii. 1947, p. 33.

91. *Bulletin*, May, 1961, p. 26.

92. *The Crayon*:

    i. Feb. 7, 1855, p. 88.
    ii. Feb. 28, 1855, p. 137.
    iii. May, 1856, p. 147.
    iv. Aug., 1856, p. 249.
    v. May, 1857, p. 158.
    vi. Dec., 1857, p. 376.
    vii. Jan., 1858, p. 26.
    viii. April, 1858, p. 116.
    ix. May, 1858, p. 148.
    x. Dec., 1858, pp. 354-55.
    xi. Jan., 1859, pp. 25, 27.
    xii. Feb., 1859, p. 58.
    xiii. Dec., 1860, p. 353.

93. Denver Art Museum, *Building the West*, Oct., 1955, pp. 9, 25, 30.

94. Edward Eberstadt & Sons, *Catalogue 139, A Distinguished Collection of Western Paintings*, New York, n. d., p. iii, No. 95.

95. Fifth Avenue Art Galleries, *Executors' Sale by Order of Mrs. S. L. Vivian and Jno. F. Patterson, Executors of the Late Marshall O. Roberts...*, New York, 1897, pp. 16, 49, 69, 79.

96. Goodrich, Lloyd, *American Genre, The Social Scene in Paintings and Prints (1800-1935)*, pp. 7-9.

97. Graham, Alexander S., « The Story of a Picture and an Artist, » *The Rutgers Alumni Monthly*, March, 1925, p. 174 and cover.

98. *Graham's Magazine*, Aug., 1855, facing p. 130.

99. Grand Central Art Galleries, Inc., *Remington to Today*, New York, 1955, No. 38.

100. *Harper's New Monthly Magazine*:

    i. Dec., 1850, p. 131.
    ii. June, 1851, p. 136.

Harry Shaw Newman Gallery:

101. *Panorama*:

    i. Oct., 1945, p. 10.
    ii. Feb., 1948, pp. 68, 71.

102. John Levy Galleries, *America in the 19th Century*, New York, 1944, No. 22.

103. John Nicholson Gallery..., *First News of the Battle of Lexington*, New York [c. 1947].

104. Joslyn Art Museum, *Life on the Prairie: The Artist's Record*, Omaha, 1954, p. 6.

105. *The Kennedy Quarterly*, Dec., 1960, p. 19.

106. *The Knickerbocker*:

    i. Dec., 1833, pp. 410-13.
    ii. March, 1845, pp. 194-5.
    iii. June, 1846, p. 556.
    iv. Nov., 1848, p. 467.
    v. May., 1854, pp. 546-7.
    vi. July, 1856, pp. 26-27, 29, 33.

107. Knoedler Galleries, *The Far West*, New York [c. 1949], Nos. 37-39.

108. Lee, Everett S., « The Turner Thesis Reëxamined, » *American Quarterly*, Spring, 1961, pp. 77-83.

109. *Life*:
   i. July 4, 1949, pp. 40, 42.
   ii. July 3, 1950, pp. 56-57.
110. *The Literary World*:
   i. March 27, 1847, pp. 182-3.
   ii. June 12, 1847, p. 447.
   iii. Oct. 23, 1847, p. 277.
   iv. Nov. 13, 1847, p. 356.
   v. April 14, 1849, p. 342.
   vi. Aug. 11, 1849, p. 113.
   vii. April 14, 1849, p. 342.
   viii. May 4, 1850, p. 448.
   ix. Sept. 28, 1850, p. 262.
   x. Dec. 21, 1850, p. 512.
   xi. May 1, 1852, p. 316.
   xii. Nov. 6, 1852, p. 300.
   xiii. Dec. 25, 1852, p. 406.
   xiv. April 30, 1853, p. 359.
111. Lyman Allyn Museum, *Eighty Eminent Painters of Connecticut*, New London, 1947, Nos. 65, 66.
112. *Magazine of Art*, May, 1945, back cover.
The Maryland Historical Society, Baltimore:
113. Exhibition *Catalogues*:
   i. 1858, p. 4.
   ii. 1901, p. 12.
   iii. 1904, p. 12.
   iv. 1907, p. 12.
114. Mather, Jr., Frank J., « American Paintings at Princeton, » *Record of the Museum of Historic Art, Princeton University*, Fall, 1943, p. 7.
115. [McNeir, Corrine] *Louisiana Paintings of the Nineteenth Century*, Baton Rouge, 1959, p. 4.
116. The Metropolitan Museum of Art, New York:
   i. *Life in America*, 1939, pp. 100-101.
   ii. *Bulletin...*, April, 1939, p. 83.
117. Miner's Art Galleries, *Catalogue of a Very Fine Assemblage of Works of Art... of Mr. Wm. H. Webb...*, New York, 1876, pp. 9, 16, 22.
118. Mint Museum of Art, *Selected Paintings*, Charlotte, 1957.
119. Modern Enterprises, *The Beale Collection*, Philadelphia, n. d.
National Academy of Design, New York:
120. Annual Exhibition *Catalogues*:
   i. 1838, p. 17.
   ii. 1845, pp. 11, 17, 28.
   iii. 1846, pp. 10, 11, 17, 22, 23, 28.
   iv. 1847, pp. 13, 21, 28.
   v. 1848, pp. 5, 7, 16.
   vi. 1850, pp. 16, 30.
   vii. 1851, pp. 5, 17, 20, 26, 33.
   viii. 1852, pp. 6, 15, 25, 35.
   ix. 1853, pp. 6, 12, 14, 25, 28, 35.
   x. 1854, pp. 6, 21, 32.
   xi. 1855, pp. 11, 20, 32.
   xii. 1856, pp. 5, 14, 17, 28.
   xiii. 1857, pp. 5, 33, 42.
121. The Newark Museum, Newark, New Jersey:
   i. *A Museum in Action*, 1944, pp. 42, 43, 85, 183.
   ii. *Early New Jersey Artists*, 1957, pp. 5, 12, 26, 32.
   iii. *Of Other Days. Scenes of Everyday Life*, 1957, n. p.
122. The Newhouse Galleries, *The Second Annual Exhibition of American Genre Paintings Depicting the Pioneer Period*, New York, 1933-34, No. 48.
123. *News from Home*, March, 1952, p. 7 and cover.
124. New York City Directories:
   i. 1843, p. 279.
   ii. 1844, p. 286.
   iii. 1845, p. 340.
   iv. 1845, p. 298.
   v. 1846, p. 322.
   vi. 1847, p. 336.
125. North Carolina Museum of Art, *Catalogue of Paintings*, Raleigh, 1956, p. 44 [W. R. Valentiner].
126. Parke-Bernet Galleries, New York:
   Catalogues:
   i. 1948, No. 80.
   ii. 1954, No. 438.
127. The Pennsylvania Academy of Fine Arts, *Catalogue... Twenty-Eighth Annual Exhibition...*, Philadelphia, 1851, p. 9.
128. Peters, Fred J., *Sporting Prints*, New York, 1930, p. 98.
129. *Portfolio*, April, 1942, pp. 22, 23.
130. The Ranney Memorial and Historical Association, *Founders, Fathers and Patriots of Middletown Upper Houses*, Middletown, 1903, n. p.
131. Rathbone, Perry T., (Ed.), *Westward the Way*, St. Louis, 1954, pp. 158, 167, 179-85, 267, 268, 277.
132. Roberts, Kenneth, « 900 Men Who Shook an Empire, » *Colliers*, Aug. 17, 1956, pp. 58-67.
133. *Saturday Review of Literature*, Oct. 20, 1951, p. 15.
134. Shaw, John G., *Statement in Relation to Estate of John Nott, Late of Cumberland County, North Carolina*, Fayetteville [c. 1910].
135. The J. B. Speed Art Museum, Louisville:
   i. *Bulletin*, Feb., 1960, n. p. [Paul S. Harris].
   ii. *Fourteen Seasons of Art Accessions 1947 to 1960*, 1960, No. 45 [Paul S. Harris].
   iii. *Bulletin*, March, 1962, n. p.
136. U. S. Department of the Interior, *Cowpens National Battlefield Site, South Carolina*, Washington, D. C., 1960, n. p.
137. U. S. Sanitary Commission, *Catalogue of Paintings, Drawings, Statuary Etc. of the Art Department in the Great Central Fair*, Philadelphia, 1864, pp. 7, 8, 10, 18.
138. Vaughan, Malcolm, « Good As Gold: Old American Paintings, » *Vogue*, Oct. 1, 1953, p. 186.
139. The Virginia Museum of Fine Arts, *An Exhibition of Nineteenth Century Virginia Genre*, Richmond, 1946, p. 12.
140. Vose Galleries, Boston:
   i. *Fourth Summer Exhibition...*, 1948, n. p.
   ii. *Catalogue, Summer Exhibition...*, 1948, Nos. 24, 36.
   iii. *A Loan Exhibition Honoring Robert Churchill Vose...*, 1961, No. 27.
141. Weitenkampf, Frank, « Currier & Ives, Picture Makers to Uncle Sam, » *Antiques*, Jan., 1925, pp. 10-14.
142. — — —, « What Is American in Early American Prints? » *American Collector*, Oct., 1948, pp. 14-16, 22.

143. Western Art-Union, *Transactions... for the Year 1850*, Cincinnati, pp. 15, 20, 71.
144. William Rockhill Nelson Gallery of Art and the Mary Atkins Museum of Fine Arts, *The Last Frontier*, Kansas City, 1957, pp. 2, 10, 20, 24.

III. NEWSPAPERS [Arranged by city]

Boston, Mass.
145. *The Christian Science Monitor*:
    i. Dec. 11, 1922.
    ii. Sept. 1, 1945.
Brooklyn, N. Y.
146. *Brooklyn Daily Eagle*:
    i. Oct. 29, 1841.
    ii. Dec. 31, 1933.
    iii. Jan. 28, 1945.
Charleston, S. C.
147. *The News And Courier*, Dec. 16, 1946.
Cincinnati, Ohio
148. *The Cincinnati Enquirer*, Jan. 22, 1851.
149. *Cincinnati Gazette*, Nov. 1, 1850.
Denver, Col.
150. *Denver Post*, Oct. 23, 1955.
Hartford, Conn.
151. *The Connecticut Courant*, Oct. 6, 1829.
Hoboken, N. J.
152. *Hoboken Gazette*, Dec. 4, 1858.
153. *Hudson Observer*, Oct., 1927.
Jersey City, N. J.
154. *Jersey Journal*, March 1, 1957.
Kansas City, Mo.
155. *Kansas City Star*, Oct. 4, 1957.
Middletown, Conn.
156. *Middlesex Gazette and General Advertiser*, March 26, 1826.
New Haven, Conn.
157. *Connecticut Herald*, May 13, 1828.
New York City, N. Y.
158. *Commercial Advertiser*, Dec. 22, 1858.
159. *The Evening Mirror*:
    i. Oct. 10, 1853.
    ii. Nov. 9, 1853.
160. *The Evening Post*:
    i. Jan. 21, 1846.
    ii. Feb. 11, 14, 25, 1846.
    iii. Nov. 20, 1857.
    iv. Dec. 2, 4, 11, 16, 20, 31, 1858.
    v. Jan. 21, 1859.
161. *Evening Post for the Country*:
    i. Aug. 13, 1832.
    ii. Sept. 3, 12, 1838.
    iii. Aug. 29, 1846.
    iv. Oct. 3, 1846.
162. *Herald*:
    i. April 23, 1845.
    ii. May 1, 3, 1845.
    iii. Nov. 2, 1845.
    iv. July 15, 1850.
    v. Aug. 13, 1850.
    vi. Sept. 8, 1850.
    vii. Dec. 5, 14, 17, 21, 1850.
    viii. May 1, 1851.
    ix. Dec. 3, 10, 1851.
    x. Feb. 17, 1852.
    xi. April 21, 1852.

    xii. Dec. 17, 18, 1852.
    xiii. May 8, 23, 30, 1853.
    xiv. Sept. 9, 20, 27, 1853.
    xv. Oct. 2, 1853.
    xvi. Nov. 7, 11, 1853.
    xvii. June 22, 1854.
    xviii. Oct. 19, 1854.
    xix. Jan. 30, 1855.
    xx. March 24, 1855.
    xxi. March 23, 24, 1857.
    xxii. April 28, 1857.
    xxiii. July 13, 1857.
    xxiv. Oct. 31, 1857.
    xxv. Nov. 20, 1857.
    xxvi. Dec. 16, 1857.
    xxvii. Jan. 1, 1858.
    xxviii. April 26, 1858.
    xxix. May 9, 1858.
    xxx. Oct. 21, 1858.
    xxxi. Dec. 3, 8, 17, 20, 23, 1858.
163. *Herald Tribune*, April 6, 1955.
164. *The Home Journal*:
    i. Nov. 25, 1848.
    ii. Nov. 25, 1849.
    iii. Dec. 8, 1849.
    iv. Nov. 9, 1850.
    v. Dec. 21, 1850.
165. *Journal of Commerce*, Dec. 18, 1858.
166. *Morning Courier and New-York Enquirer*:
    i. March 28, 1849.
    ii. Aug. 18, 1849.
    iii. Dec. 20, 21, 24, 1858.
167. *Morning Express*:
    i. Nov. 10, 1853.
    ii. Oct. 30, 1857.
    iii. Nov. 20, 21, 1857.
168. *The National Advocate*:
    i. June 6, 1828.
    ii. Nov. 21, 1828.
169. *New-York Enquirer*:
    i. Nov. 27, 1827.
    ii. Jan. 21, 1828.
    iii. Feb. 28, 1828.
    iv. March 4, 6, 14, 29, 1828.
    v. April 1, 4, 1828.
    vi. May 8, 1828.
    vii. June 6, 1828.
170. *Sun*:
    i. May 28, 1938.
    ii. Feb. 25, 1949.
171. *Times*:
    i. Nov. 24, 1857.
    ii. Dec. 5, 9, 10, 17, 20, 1858.
    iii. Jan. 20, 1859.
    iv. April 23, 1939.
172. *Tribune*:
    i. Nov. 25, 1842.
    ii. April 1, 1843.
    iii. Jan. 20, 1846.
    iv. Feb. 2, 9, 12, 23, 1846.
    v. March 10, 1846.
    vi. April 24, 1846.
    vii. Oct. 1, 1846.
    viii. Sept. 1, 1849.
    ix. Dec. 4, 5, 22, 1849.

x. April 6, 1850.
xi. May 14, 1850.
xii. June 22, 1850.
xiii. Sept. 5, 1850.
xiv. Nov. 27, 1850.
xv. Dec. 10, 16, 21, 1850.
xvi. April 23, 1851.
xvii. May 7, 1851.
xviii. June 21, 1851.
xix. Dec. 5, 1851.
xx. Dec. 17, 18, 1852.
xxi. Sept. 8, 9, 16, 20, 27, 1853.
xxii. Oct. 4, 13, 15, 1853.
xxiii. Oct. 18, 19, 28, 31, 1853.
xxiv. Nov. 1, 1854.
xxv. Nov. 2, 6, 1857.
xxvi. Dec. 17, 21, 1858.
xxvii. Jan. 20, 1859.
xxviii. Feb. 16, 1866.
xxix. Feb. 23, 1867.
xxx. Dec. 23, 1876.
xxxi. Jan. 20, 21, 1897.

173. *Weekly Evening Post*, Nov. 16, 1848.
Philadelphia, Pa.

174. *Inquirer*:
i. Jan. 18, 1949.
ii. April 6, 1958.
Richmond, Va.

175. *Times Dispatch*, Jan. 26, 1946.
St. Louis, Mo.

176. *Post-Dispatch*, Oct. 31, 1954.

IV. MANUSCRIPT MATERIAL

177. The Corcoran Gallery of Art, Washington, D. C.:
i. « Accession Record Sheet, » No. 69.62, n. d.
ii. « Objects No Longer in the Gallery, A-J, » n. d.
iii. « 1. Register of Paintings Belonging to the Corcoran Gallery of Art: 1869-1940. »
iv. « Report. Committee on Works of Art to the Board of Trustees, April 17, 1911. »
v. « Scultpture and Paintings from the Private Collection of W. W. Corcoran Given to the Corcoran Gallery, » May 13, 1958.

178. The Mechanics' Institute of the City of New York, « Diploma, » Fair of 1838, awarded to William Ranny [sic]. In the Collection of Claude J. Ranney, Malvern, Pennsylvania.

179. Mystic Maritime Museum, Mystic, Connecticut, « Items pertaining to [Captain] William Ranney, 1810-27 » [Courtesy Thomas A. Stevens].

180. New-York Historical Society, *The Ranney Collection*. One scrapbook bound volume containing a copy of the *Catalogue of Paintings to Be Sold for the Benefit of the Ranney Fund*, [1858] with inscriptions in ink of prices and owners; also clippings, notices and other material pertaining to the sale, and to the death of the artist, including the unidentified clipping referred to as G. H., « Death of William Ranney. »

181. New York Public Library, « The William Tylee Ranney File, » which contains the « Questionnaire for *Appletons' Cyclopaedia of American Biography*, » completed c. 1883 by the artist's wife, Margaret Ranney; also clippings, engravings and reproductions.

182. New-York Southern District, « Copyright Records, » Library of Congress, Washington, D. C.:
i. Vol. 161, No. 7399, Jan. 24, 1852.
ii. Vol. 162, No. 7460, Feb. 12, 1852.

183. « Notes Compiled by Mr. Claude J. Ranney, Malvern, Pennsylvania. »

184. Office of Probated Wills, Trenton, New Jersey, « Will of Sophia C. V. C. Stevens, Princeton, New Jersey, May 28, 1888, Register No. 5222. »

185. Texas State Archives, Texas State Library and Historical Commission, Austin, Texas, Comptroller's Military Service Records, « Military Service Record of William Ranney: Nos. 990, 1409, 1509, and Receipt of Nov. 23, 1836. »

V. MISCELLANEOUS MATERIAL

186. American Heritage, Ad. Envelope, c. 1957.

187. Life Filmstrips, « The American Revolution, » [with lecture notes], New York, 1950.

188. Provident Mutual Life Insurance Company, Calendar. Philadelphia, February, 1941.

189. West Virginia Pulp and Paper Company, Calendar. New York, 1947.

6   THE BATTLE OF COWPENS - Dr. J. Lewi Donhauser, Albany, New York.

11 THE MATCH BOY - Mr. Francis S. Grubar, Washington, D. C.

20   THE LASSO - Mr. Claude J. Ranney, Malvern, Pennsylvania.

25 SLEIGHING - Mr. and Mrs. J. Maxwell Moran, Paoli, Pennsylvania.

21   HUNTING WILD HORSES · M. Knoedler and Company, New York.

26 FIRST NEWS OF THE BATTLE OF LEXINGTON · The North Carolina Museum of Art, Raleigh, North Carolina.

30 PRAIRIE BURIAL - Mr. and Mrs. J. Maxwell Moran, Paoli, Pennsylvania.

32 THE PRAIRIE FIRE - Mr. and Mrs. J. Maxwell Moran, Paoli, Pennsylvania.

36 DUCK SHOOTERS - Museum of Fine Arts, Boston, Karolik Collection.

42 THE TRAPPER'S LAST SHOT · Mr. C. R. Smith, New York.

44   HALT ON THE PRAIRIE - Mr. C. R. Smith, New York.

46   ON THE WING - J. N. Bartfield, Inc.

47   THE PIONEERS - Mr. Claude J. Ranney, Malvern, Pennsylvania.

48   DUCK SHOOTING - The Corcoran Gallery of Art, Washington, D. C.

49 HALT ON THE PRAIRIE - Mr. and Mrs. John F. Merriam, Omaha, Nebraska.

51   THE RETREAT - M. Knoedler and Company, New York.

52 PORTRAIT OF MARGARET RANNEY, WIFE OF THE ARTIST - Mr. Claude J. Ranney, Malvern, Pennsylvania.

57 THE TRAPPERS - M. Knoedler and Company, New York.

59   THE OLD OAKEN BUCKET · M. Knoedler and Company, New York.

60 THE SCOUTING PARTY - M. Knoedler and Company, New York.

61 THE SCOUTING PARTY - Mr. Claude J. Ranney, Malvern, Pennsylvania.

66 SQUIRE BOONE CROSSING THE MOUNTAINS WITH STORES FOR HIS BROTHER DANIEL, ENCAMPED IN THE WILDS OF KENTUCKY - Miss Amelia Peabody, Boston, Massachusetts.

68   ADVICE ON THE PRAIRIE - Mr. Claude J. Ranney, Malvern, Pennsylvania.

71 A TRAPPER CROSSING THE MOUNTAINS - The J. B. Speed Art Museum, Louisville, Kentucky.

86 HALT ON THE PLAINS - Mrs. Eleanor Searle Whitney, Long Island, New York.

87 SELF-PORTRAIT - Mr. Claude J. Ranney, Malvern, Pennsylvania.

89 THE TORY ESCORT - Miss Margaret Ranney, Union City, New Jersey.

110 STUDY OF A LEDGE - Mr. Claude J. Ranney, Malvern, Pennsylvania.

123   THREE FISHERMEN IN A SKIFF - The Corcoran Gallery of Art, Washington, D. C.

W.T. RANNEY, A.N.A.
1813 ~ 1857

124   DRAGOON WITH HIS CHARGER - The Corcoran Gallery of Art, Washington, D. C.

125 TOOTH EXTRACTION · The Corcoran Gallery of Art, Washington, D. C.

126 PIONEER CARAVAN - Mr. Claude J. Ranney, Malvern, Pennsylvania.

128   STUDY FOR 'FIRST NEWS OF THE BATTLE OF LEXINGTON' - Mr. Claude J. Ranney, Malvern, Pennsylvania.

129   STUDY FOR 'ON THE WING' - Mr. Claude J. Ranney, Malvern, Pennsylvania.

130 STUDY FOR 'HUNTING WILD HORSES' · Mr. Claude J. Ranney, Malvern, Pennsylvania.

131　CALLING THE HOUNDS · Mr. Claude J. Ranney, Malvern, Pennsylvania.

132 FRONTIER HORSE AUCTION · Mr. Claude J. Ranney, Malvern, Pennsylvania.

134 GIST RESCUING WASHINGTON FROM THE ALLEGHENY RIVER - Mr. Claude J. Ranney, Malvern, Pennsylvania.

135   RIVER SCENE WITH BOY FISHING - Mr. Claude J. Ranney, Malvern, Pennsylvania.

137 DUCK SHOOTERS - Mr. Claude J. Ranney, Malvern, Pennsylvania.

138   THE PRANKSTER - Mr. Claude J. Ranney, Malvern, Pennsylvania.

139 COAST SCENE WITH TWO FIGURES - Mr. Claude J. Ranney, Malvern, Pennsylvania.

140   WASHINGTON WITH SOLDIERS - Mr. Claude J. Ranney, Malvern, Pennsylvania.

141   THREE BOATS ON THE BEACH - Mr. Claude J. Ranney, Malvern, Pennsylvania.

147 STUDY OF TWO OAK TREES · Mr. Claude J. Ranney, Malvern, Pennsylvania.

148   STUDY FOR 'THE RETREAT' - Mr. Claude J. Ranney, Malvern, Pennsylvania.

149   COUNTRY BRIDGE NEAR MIDDLETOWN, CONNENTICUT - Mr. Claude J. Ranney, Malvern, Pennsylvania.

150 LANDSCAPE WITH TREES AND ROCKS - Mr. Claude J. Ranney, Malvern, Pennsylvania.

152   WEEPING WILLOW - Mr. Claude J. Ranney, Malvern, Pennsylvania.

158 GEORGE WASHINGTON CONVERSING WITH A WOMAN - Mr. Claude J. Ranney, Malvern, Pennsylvania.

162 LANDSCAPE WITH HORSEMAN - Mr. Claude J. Ranney, Malvern, Pennsylvania.

167 TWO TREES - Mr. Claude J. Ranney, Malvern, Pennsylvania.

171 FIELD WITH TREES - Mr. Claude J. Ranney, Malvern, Pennsylvania.

178 TWO SKETCHES OF A MAN POLING - Mr. Claude J. Ranney, Malvern, Pennsylvania.

NO